DIRECTORY OF FUNCTIONS AND PROCEDURES

■

AUXILIARY FUNCTIONS

DISTRIBUTIONS

MINTERM VECTORS AND PROBABILITIES

INDEPENDENT EVENTS

CONDITIONAL PROBABILITY AND CONDITIONAL INDEPENDENCE

BERNOULLI AND MULTINOMIAL TRIALS

SIMPLE RANDOM VARIABLES

JOINT SIMPLE RANDOM VARIABLES

DISCRETE APPROXIMATION

RANDOM SUMS

BookWare Companion Series
≡

Published and Forthcoming Volumes

BookWare Companions
—————◼————

Cullen/Molina, Communication Systems Using MATLAB

Dickinson/Boncelet, Introduction to Linear Algebra Using MATLAB (0-534-93810-8)

Friedland/Chang, Feedback Control Systems Using MATLAB

Harman, Advanced Mathematical Analysis (0-534-94350-0)

Larimore, System Identification with Adapt using MATLAB (0-534-93807-8)

Saltsburg, Problem Solving for Engineers (0-534-93828-0)

Strum/Kirk, Contemporary Linear Systems Using MATLAB (0-534-93273-8) **Published**

Strum/Kirk/Therrien, Digital Signal Processing Using MATLAB (0-534-93806-X)

Tummala, Probabilistic Analysis of Signals and Systems Using MATLAB (0-534-93816-7)

Wood, Image Processing Using MATLAB (0-534-93991-0)

BookWare Companion Problems Books
—————◼————

Frederick/Chow, Feedback Control Problems Using MATLAB (0-534-93798-5)

Pfeiffer, Basic Probability Topics Using MATLAB (0-534-94536-8) **Published**

Proakis/Ingle, Digital Signal Processing Problems Using MATLAB (0-534-93805-1)

Proakis/Salehi, Introduction to Communications Systems Using MATLAB (0-534-93804-3)

BookWare Companion Notebooks

Dabney, Maple Notebook to accompany Advanced Mathematical Analysis (0-534-94351-9)

Evans, Mathematica Notebook to accompany Contemporary Linear Systems Using MATLAB Version 1.1

Rickert, Mathematica Notebook to accompany Advanced Mathematical Analysis (0-534-943527)

BookWare Companion Lab Manuals

Stonick/Bradley, Labs for Signals and Systems Using MATLAB (0-534-93808-6)

A Production Note: This book has been published using a completely electronic production process. The author submitted his manuscript on computer disks prepared in LaTeX. The LaTeX files were converted into SGML by Beacon Graphics. This is a comprehensive conversion that includes all text and math equations. Once all copy was prepared for publication the final product was complete SGML and PostScript files. This process assures exact use of the author's material; reduces the time and cost of production; and allows the publisher flexibility to offer printed material in alternative formats such as CD-ROM or on-line services.

About the Cover: The BookWare Companion Series cover was created on a Macintosh Quadra 700, using Aldus FreeHand and Quark XPress. The surface plot on the cover, provided courtesy of The MathWorks, Inc., Natick, MA, was created with MATLAB® and was inserted on the cover mockup with a HP ScanJet IIP Scanner. It represents a surface created by assigning the values of different functions to specific matrix elements.

A BC Note

Students learn in a number of ways and in a variety of settings. They learn through lectures, in informal study groups, or alone at their desks or in front of a computer terminal. Wherever the location, students learn most efficiently by solving problems, with frequent feedback from an instructor, following a worked-out problem as a model. Worked-out problems have a number of positive aspects. They can capture the essence of a key concept—often better than paragraphs of explanation. They provide methods for acquiring new knowledge and for evaluating its use. They provide a taste of real-life issues and demonstrate techniques for solving real problems. Most importantly, they encourage active participation in learning.

We created the BookWare Companion Series because we saw an unfulfilled need for computer-based learning tools that address the computational aspects of problem solving across the curriculum. The BC series concept was also shaped by other forces: A general agreement among instructors that students learn best when they are actively involved in their own learning, and the realization that textbooks have not kept up with or matched student learning needs. Educators and publishers are just beginning to understand that the amount of material crammed into most textbooks cannot be absorbed, let alone the knowledge to be mastered in four years of undergraduate study. Rather than attempting to teach students all the latest knowledge, colleges and universities are now striving to teach them to reason: to understand the relationships and connections between new information and existing knowledge; and to cultivate problem-solving skills, intuition, and critical thinking. The BookWare Companion Series was developed in response to this changing mission.

Specifically, the BookWare Companion Series was designed for educators who wish to integrate their curriculum with computer-based learning tools, and for students who find their current textbooks overwhelming. The former will find in the BookWare Companion Series the means by which to use powerful software tools to support their course activities, without having to customize the applications themselves. The latter will find relevant problems and examples quickly and easily and have instant electronic access to them.

We hope that the BC series will become a clearing house for the exchange of reliable teaching ideas and a baseline series for incorporating learning advances from emerging technologies. For example, we intend to reuse the kernel of each BC volume and add electronic scripts from other software programs as desired by customers. We are pursuing the addition of AI/Expert System technology to provide an intelligent tutoring capability for future iterations of BC volumes. We also anticipate a paperless environment in which BC content can flow freely over high-speed networks to support remote learning activities. In order for these and other goals to be realized, educators, students, software developers, network administrators and publishers will need to communicate freely and actively with each other. We encourage you to participate in these exciting developments and become involved in the BC Series today. If you have an idea for improving the effectiveness of the BC concept, an example problem, a demonstration using software or multimedia, or an opportunity to explore, contact us (an insert card for your feedback is attached in the back of this volume).

Cheers,

Robert D. Strum, Series Editor
71052.2672@Compuserve.Com

Tom Robbins, Acquisitions Editor
Tom_Robbins@PWS.Com

Pam Rockwell, Production
Pam_Rockwell@PWS.Com

Ken Morton, Assistant Editor
Ken_Morton@PWS.Com

Nathan Wilbur, Marketing Manager
Nathan_Wilbur@PWS.Com

Cynthia Harris, Editorial Assistant
Cynthia_Harris@PWS.Com

Lisa Flanagan
Manufacturing

Tom Robbins'

BookWare Companion Series™

Basic Probability

Using MATLAB®

Paul E. Pfeiffer
Rice University

PWS Publishing Company

I(T)P An International Thomson Publishing Company

Boston · Albany · Bonn · Cincinnati · Detroit · London · Madrid · Melbourne
Mexico City · New York · Paris · San Francisco · Singapore · Tokyo · Toronto
Washington

PWS Publishing Company

MATLAB and PC MATLAB are trademarks of The Mathworks, Inc. The MathWorks, Inc. is the developer of MATLAB, the high-performance computational software introduced in this book. For further information on MATLAB and other MathWorks products—including SIMULINK™ and MATLAB Application Toolboxes for math and analysis, control system design, system identification, and other disciplines—contact The MathWorks at 24 Prim Park Way, Natick, MA 01760 (phone: 508-653-1415; fax: 508-653-2997; email: info@mathworks.com). You can also sign up to receive The MathWorks quarterly newsletter and register for the user group.
Macintosh is a trademark of Apple Computer, Inc.
MS-DOS is a trademark of Microsoft Corporation.
BookWare Companion Series is a trademark of PWS Publishing Company.

I(T)P ™
International Thomson Publishing
The trademark ITP is used under license

For more information, contact:

PWS Publishing Co.
20 Park Plaza
Boston, MA 02116

International Thomson Publishing Europe
Berkshire House I68-I73
High Holborn
London WC1V7AA
England

Thomas Nelson Australia
102 Dodds Street
South Melbourne, 3205
Victoria, Australia

Nelson Canada
1120 Birchmount Road
Scarborough, Ontario
Canada M1K 5G4

International Thomson Editores
Campos Eliseos 385, Piso 7
Col. Polanco
11560 Mexico C.F., Mexico

International Thomson Publishing GmbH
Konigswinterer Strasse 418
53227 Bonn, Germany

International Thomson Publishing Asia
221 Henderson Road
#05-10 Henderson Building
Singapore 0315

International Thomson Publishing Japan
Hirakawacho Kyyowa Building, 31
2-2-1 Hirakawacho
Chiyoda-ku, Tokyo 102
Japan

Series Co-originators: Tom Robbins and
Robert D. Strum
Assistant Editor: Ken Morton
Editorial Assistant: Cynthia Harris
Marketing Manager: Nathan Wilbur
Production: Pamela Rockwell

Manufacturing Coordinator: Lisa Flanagan
Cover Designer: Stuart Paterson, Image House, Inc.
Compositor: Eigentype Compositors, Inc.
Cover Printer: Henry N. Sawyer, Inc.
Text Printer and Binder: Malloy Lithographing

  This book is printed on recycled, acid-free paper.

Printed and bound in the United States of America
94 95 96 97 98 99 – 10 9 8 7 6 5 4 3 2 1

Contents

2 Conditional Probability, Independence, and Conditional Independence   37

3 Random Variables and Distributions   73

4 Simple Random Variables 99

CONTENTS

CONTENTS

CONTENTS

Preface

A SUPPLEMENTARY TEXT

■

This book describes and employs user defined MATLAB procedures and functions (which we refer to simply as *programs*) to solve many important problems in basic probability. Although growing out of a course based on my text *Probability for Applications,* Springer, 1990 (referred to as *PA*), this work should be useful as a supplement to any of several current texts. The reader should have an acquaintance with elementary calculus and the rudiments of matrices in linear algebra.

As a supplementary text, the book treats only topics for which the computational power of MATLAB is useful. In writing it, I have generally assumed that the basic mathematical system has been introduced, that the central concepts have been presented and interpreted, and that some practice in formulating problems in terms of this model and in interpreting the results has been provided. In most cases, "small" elementary problems will have been solved "by hand," with the aid of hand calculators.

Many significant problems require appropriate formulation and formal analysis, with very little computation. I do not treat such problems, since the computational power of MATLAB is not needed.

On the other hand, the solutions of some problems require considerable computation. It is for many of these that MATLAB provides convenient, easily used, but powerful tools. Computational results often reveal patterns and produce insights that theoretical analysis alone cannot achieve. This is particularly true when easy computation allows exploration of a variety of cases, and perhaps a variety of solution strategies, for comparison.

In a few cases, principally in Chapters 1 and 7, it has seemed desirable to provide analytical background for topics not ordinarily included in current texts. The formal material is intended for those who desire a sound grounding in the methods. It may be treated cursorily, if at all, by those who plan to use the programs merely as computational aids to exposition, illustration, and exploration.

MATLAB VERSIONS
———————————————■———

Currently (early 1994) versions 3.5 and 4.1 are in common use. Many of the programs in this book were written under 3.5 but work without change in 4.1. Even when version 4.1 has newer (and usually preferred) conventions, there are alternatives which work in both versions. The principal exception has been functions for the gamma and gaussian distributions. In those cases, I have provided on the disk alternate script for version 3.5. Because version 3.5 has no incomplete beta function, the beta distribution function cannot be implemented.

Version 4.1 has extensive graphics capabilities not available on the earlier version. This should cause no problem, since we use only plots of simple 2-D graphs.

The full professional edition of version 4.1 is available for MS-DOS and Macintosh personal computers as well as the usual workstation operating systems. *Student editions* for MS-DOS machines and Macintoshes are available in version 3.5, with upgrades to version 4.1 either available or planned for the near future. Older student editions limit matrix sizes to 32 × 32, and the MS-DOS version has very limited graphics. However, given the rapid pace of change, the user should investigate the situation at the time of purchase. At any rate, most of the programs included with this text should work well on the earlier student editions provided size limitations are not exceeded.

A TOOL FOR LEARNING
———————————————■———

I have tried to write the MATLAB programs in such a way that they constitute useful, ready-made tools for problem solving. Once the user understands the problems they are designed to solve, the solution strategies used, and the manner in which these strategies are implemented, the collection of programs should provide a useful resource.

However, my primary aim in exposition and illustration is to *aid the learning process* and to deepen insight into the structure of the problems considered and the strategies employed in their solution. Several features contribute to that end.

1. Application of machine methods of solution requires precise
   formulation. The data available and the fundamental assumptions

must be organized in an appropriate fashion. The requisite *discipline* often contributes to enhanced understanding of the problem.

2. The development of a MATLAB program for solution requires careful attention to possible solution strategies. One cannot instruct the machine without a clear grasp of what is to be done.

3. I give attention to the tasks performed by a program with a general description of how MATLAB carries out the tasks. The reader is not required to trace out all the programming details. However, it is often the case that available MATLAB resources suggest alternative solution strategies. Hence, for those so inclined, attention to the details may be fruitful.

4. Many of the details in the MATLAB script are presentation details. These are refinements which are not essential to the solution of the problem, but they make the programs more readily usable. And they provide illustrations of MATLAB techniques for those who may wish to write their own programs. I hope many will be inclined to go beyond this work, modifying current programs or writing new ones.

AN INVITATION TO EXPERIMENT AND EXPLORE

Because the programs provide considerable freedom from the burden of computation and the tyranny of tables (with their limited ranges and parameter values), standard problems may be approached with a new spirit of inquisitiveness and discovery.

1. When a program is selected (or written), it embodies one method of solution. There may be others which can be readily implemented. The reader is invited, even urged, to explore!

2. For example, when the joint distribution for a pair $\{X, Y\}$ of random variables is given, the standard questions may be amplified and extended in many ways.

   a. If the probability that the pair takes on a particular set of values is asked for, the same question can be asked about many other interesting possible sets of values.

   b. If the expectation of Y is sought, this may be calculated in various ways: using the marginal distribution; using the joint distribution; or by using the law of total probability, which says the expectation of Y is the expectation of the conditional expectation of Y, given X. Each method has its role in probability theory; each possibility may be examined and the results compared.

   c. When the distribution or expectation of a *function* of $\{X, Y\}$ is determined, the same determination may be made for other interesting functions. Once again, more than one way of solving the problem at hand may be examined.

3. Another kind of comparison is suggested in the problem of compound or comparative Bernoulli trials. Such problems may be solved either in terms of combinations of events or in terms of independent random variables. Solutions in both formulations should be carried out and results compared. The added insight can be obtained with a minimum of computational tedium.

The possibilities are endless. The user may experiment to whatever degree he or she finds useful and interesting.

A PERSONAL NOTE—A WORK IN PROGRESS

Although there were some antecedents, most of this material has either been developed "from scratch" or significantly modified and improved over a period of some eighteen months. As the programs were developed and introduced to my students, both I and many of them have found the fascinating topic of probability taking on new life. After more than forty years of teaching probability, I have been surprised and pleased at how much the development of these programs has added to my own perspective and insight. I am sure that my presentation of the fundamental ideas has improved, and certainly the quality of the problems and examples has profited. I believe both new students and experienced teachers may have a similar experience of enhanced learning.

Several times I have felt the work was essentially completed, given the constraints of planned length and completion date, only to have new programs or significant improvements to older programs suggest themselves. Although I believe this to be a very useful and reasonably mature collection of programs and examples, this is very much a "work in progress." The reader is encouraged to continue that work of discovery and exploration.

Although MATLAB is powerful and versatile, it is easy to use. One need not be a master programmer to find new ways to use MATLAB. If so, I could not have developed the programs in this book. Once a problem is posed carefully and possible solutions procedures are considered, it is highly likely that a MATLAB implementation (perhaps several) can be found. Try it! You will like it!

One of the contributions of computer technology has been the linking of the scientific and educational community by e-mail. I should be most pleased to have responses from readers of this work. Certainly, corrections of inevitable errors would be appreciated. But questions about or suggestions for improvement would be even more satisfying. The goal is to enhance teaching. If something worked well for you, I and others might find it useful. I invite your response by mail or e-mail. My e-mail address is

pep@rice.edu

ACKNOWLEDGMENTS

After many years of teaching probability, I have long since lost track of all those authors and books which have contributed to the background for this work. I am aware of those contributions and am most eager to acknowledge my indebtedness, although necessarily without specific attribution.

The power and utility of MATLAB must be attributed to the long-time commitment of Cleve Moler. I am particularly indebted to John Dennis, a colleague, who encouraged me to try MATLAB. The appearance of the professional versions, with extended power and improved documentation, led to further appreciation of its potential in applied probability.

An important breakthrough came when a student, Geoffrey Coram, suggested a way to generate the minterm vectors that play a key role in many of the programs. Although better ways to generate these vectors have been found and many other MATLAB resources have been discovered, his contribution provided a stimulus that led, first gradually then at an accelerating rate, to the development of the programs presented herein.

I also am grateful to the following reviewers of the book:

Edward Kolesar   Paul Scheets
Texas Christian University   *Oklahoma State University*

A. Raza Moghaddamjoo   Jay Wertzeu
University of Wisconsin—Milwaukee *University of Massachusetts—Lowell*

The decision to write this book was due in large part to the vision, initiative, and enthusiasm of Tom Robbins of PWS Publishing Company. His goal of enhancing engineering and scientific education with the appropriate use of software packages such as MATLAB and MAPLE led to the Bookware Companion series.

Paul E. Pfeiffer

PREFACE

The Probability of Events

PREVIEW

As a supplementary text, this work deals primarily with certain computational aspects of basic probability, and assumes the conceptual and interpretive background has been established in the principal text. However, since the notation and terminology used in formulating the underlying model vary among authors, we summarize the essential features of the scheme used herein. In addition, certain special analytical features used in the present work are developed in sufficient detail to supplement most current texts.

In the present chapter, we introduce the *minterms* generated by a finite class of events and the *minterm expansion* of any combination of these events. Our formulation leads naturally to the concept of *minterm vectors*. These concepts display essential structural features of the problems studied, and play a central role in formulating solution strategies. In particular, minterm vectors often serve as key elements of the user defined MATLAB procedures and functions which implement the computational aspects of those strategies. More detailed development of the minterm concept may be found in the author's *Probability for Applications,* Springer, 1990 (*PA*). An earlier treatment may be found in the Dover reprint *Concepts of Probability Theory* (*CPT*).

1. THE UNDERLYING MODEL

■

PROBABILITY SYSTEMS

What do we mean by *probability?*

A number between 0 and 1 which indicates the *likelihood* that an event will occur.

There are various interpretations. Each can be supported by the same mathematical model, often known as the *Kolmogorov model,* named after the great Russian mathematician who first succeeded in providing a general and precise formulation.

What do we mean by an *event?*

There is a *trial* or experiment which results in one element of a *basic set* Ω of possible *outcomes* ω.

Event A is a *subset* of outcomes with a prescribed *property*.

A trial is performed; the outcome ω is observed. If the outcome has the property defining subset A, we say the event A has *occurred* (if not, then the complementary event A^c has occurred).

Suppose we consider two events, A and B (determined by different defining properties).

- If the outcome has both properties, ω is in both A and B, and we say *both A and B* have occurred. The joint event is represented by the subset $AB = A \cap B$.
- If the outcome has at least one (possibly both) of the properties, then $\omega \in A \cup B$, and we say *A or B* (possibly both) has occurred.
- We find it convenient to designate the union (the "or" combination) of events in the case they are mutually exclusive by the symbol $A \uplus B$. This is not a new logical combination; it is merely a convenient shorthand for $A \cup B$ with the stipulation that $AB = \varnothing$ (i.e., that A and B have no common part and hence represent events that are mutually exclusive).

We can consider larger classes of events (subsets) and more complicated logical (or Boolean) combinations. Combinations of events and the relationships between them can be represented by *Venn diagrams*. We consider in Section 2 special Venn diagrams, known as minterm maps, which aid in a systematic handling of events for machine calculations.

The discussion above indicates we must have a *basic space* Ω of elementary outcomes ω, and a class **F** of *events* which allows appropriate Boolean combinations. *Probabilities* are numbers assigned to events (subsets of Ω which are in the class **F**). An assignment of probabilities to events amounts to determining a *function* P on the class **F** of events. To each event $A \in$ **F**, we assign the number $P(A)$. A *probability system* consists of a triple $(\Omega, \mathbf{F}, P)$.

The assignment of probabilities must obey certain basic rules in order to yield a consistent and precise working theory. We take our clues from observed *statistical regularities* and from the *classical case*, which assumes a finite set of N equally likely possible outcomes. *Three properties have been identified as fundamental;* other quite basic properties can be derived from these. The function P is a *probability measure* iff it has the following properties, taken as axiomatic:

(P1) $P(A) \geq 0$ (Probability is nonnegative.)

(P2) $P(\Omega) = 1$ (Probability of the sure event is one.)

(P3) If $A = \bigcup_{k=1}^{\infty} A_k$ (disjoint union), then $P(A) = \sum_{k=1}^{\infty} P(A_k)$ (Countable additivity)

These properties imply that probability can be interpreted as *mass* associated with various events. The total mass assigned to the whole space Ω is one. Mass is nonnegative, and the mass of the union of two or more mutually exclusive (disjoint) events is the sum of the individual masses.

From the defining or axiomatic properties, we may derive other fundamental properties. Purely formal arguments are readily visualized in terms of the mass interpretation. Among the more important derived properties for our purposes are the following:

(P4) $P(A^c) = 1 - P(A)$

(P5) $P(\emptyset) = 0$

(P6) $A \subset B$ (occurrence of A implies occurrence of B) $P(A) \leq P(B)$

(P7) $P(A \cup B) = P(A) + P(B) - P(AB)$
$$= P(A) + P(A^cB) = P(B) + P(AB^c)$$
$$= P(AB^c) + P(AB) + P(A^cB)$$

A FUNDAMENTAL PROBLEM

For a finite class of basic events:

- The probabilities of certain Boolean combinations are given.
- The probabilities of other combinations are sought.

EXAMPLE 1.1
Survey on Software

Statistical data are taken for a certain student population with personal computers. An individual is selected at random. Let $A =$ the event the person selected has word processing, $B =$ the event he or she has a spreadsheet program, and $C =$ the event the person has a data base program. The data imply:

- The probability is 0.80 that the person has a *word processing program*—$P(A) = 0.8$.
- The probability is 0.65 that the person has a *spreadsheet program*—$P(B) = 0.65$.
- The probability is 0.30 that the person has a *data base program*—$P(C) = 0.3$.
- The probability is 0.10 that the person has *all three*—$P(ABC) = 0.1$.
- The probability is 0.65 that the person has *at least two*—$P(AB \cup AC \cup BC) = 0.65$.
- The probability is 0.05 that the person has *neither word processing nor spreadsheet*—$P(A^c B^c) = 0.05$.
- The probability of *word processor and data base, but no spreadsheet* is twice the probability of *spreadsheet and data base, but no word processor*—$P(AB^c C) = 2P(A^c BC)$.

(a) What is the probability that the person has exactly two of the programs?

(b) What is the probability that the person has only the data base program?

Several questions arise:

- Are these data consistent?
- Are the data sufficient to answer the questions?
- How may the data be utilized to answer the questions?

We develop a method of analysis to answer these questions. In this case, we find that the data are consistent and sufficient, and the answers are

$$P(ABC^c \uplus AB^c C \uplus A^c BC) = 0.55 \quad \text{and} \quad P(A^c B^c C) = 0.05$$

The method employed provides the basis for a MATLAB procedure to carry out the analysis.

─────────────────●

2. MINTERMS AND BOOLEAN COMBINATIONS OF EVENTS

In this section, we introduce an analysis of Boolean combinations of events that provides the basis for many of the computational procedures developed in this text.

MINTERMS AND THE MINTERM EXPANSION

We consider a systematic expansion of any Boolean combination of a finite class of events. If we partition an event F into component events whose probabilities can be determined, then additivity implies that the probability of F is the sum of these component probabilities. Frequently, the event F is a Boolean combination of members of a finite class—say, $\{A, B, C\}$ or $\{A, B, C, D\}$. For each such finite class, there is a *fundamental partition* generated by the class. The members of this partition are called *minterms*. As the name suggests, these are the fundamental building blocks for Boolean combinations of the basic events in the generating class. In fact, we show below that any Boolean combination of members of the class can be expressed as the union of a unique subclass of the minterms. If the probability of every minterm in this subclass can be determined, then, by additivity, the probability of any Boolean combination is determined. We examine these ideas in more detail.

Consider, for example, the case of four events $\{A, B, C, D\}$. We form the minterms by taking intersections of the members of the class, with various patterns of complementation. For a class of four events, there are $2^4 = 16$ such patterns, hence 16 minterms. These are, in a systematic arrangement,

$$
\begin{array}{llll}
A^c B^c C^c D^c & A^c B C^c D^c & A B^c C^c D^c & A B C^c D^c \\
A^c B^c C^c D & A^c B C^c D & A B^c C^c D & A B C^c D \\
A^c B^c C\, D^c & A^c B C\, D^c & A B^c C\, D^c & A B C\, D^c \\
A^c B^c C\, D & A^c B C\, D & A B^c C\, D & A B C\, D
\end{array}
$$

These sets form a *partition* (some of the minterms could be empty). Each element ω is assigned to exactly one of the minterms by determining the answers to four questions:

Is it in A?   Is it in B?   Is it in C?   Is it in D?

Suppose, for example, the answers are: Yes, No, No, Yes. Then ω is in the minterm $A B^c C^c D$. In a similar way, we can determine the membership of each ω in the basic space. The result is thus a partition. The minterms represent mutually exclusive events, one of which is sure to occur on each trial. The membership of any minterm depends upon the membership of each generating set A, B, C, or D, and the relationships between them. For some classes, one or more of the minterms are empty (impossible events). In deriving an expression for a given Boolean combination which holds for any class $\{A, B, C, D\}$ of four events, we include all possible minterms. If a minterm is empty for a given class, its presence does not modify the set content or probability assignment for the Boolean combination.

It should be clear that if we begin with a class of n events, then there are 2^n minterms. To aid in systematic analysis, we introduce a simple numbering system for the minterms, which we illustrate by considering again the four events A, B, C, D, in that order. The answers to the four questions above can be represented numerically by the scheme

No ~ 0 and   Yes ~ 1

Thus, if ω is in $A^c B^c C^c D^c$, the answers are tabulated as $0\,0\,0\,0$. If ω is in $A B^c C^c D$, then this is designated $1\,0\,0\,1$. With this scheme, the minterm arrangement above becomes

$$
\begin{array}{llll}
0000 \sim 0 & 0100 \sim 4 & 1000 \sim 8 & 1100 \sim 12 \\
0001 \sim 1 & 0101 \sim 5 & 1001 \sim 9 & 1101 \sim 13 \\
0010 \sim 2 & 0110 \sim 6 & 1010 \sim 10 & 1110 \sim 14 \\
0011 \sim 3 & 0111 \sim 7 & 1011 \sim 11 & 1111 \sim 15
\end{array}
$$

We may view these quadruples of zeros and ones as binary representations of integers, which also may be represented by their decimal equivalents, as shown in the table above. Frequently, it is useful to refer to the minterms by number. If the members of the generating class are treated in a fixed order, then each minterm number arrived at in the manner illustrated above specifies a minterm uniquely. Thus, for the generating class $\{A, B, C, D\}$, in that order, we may designate

$$
A^c B^c C^c D^c = M_0 \text{ (minterm 0)} \qquad AB^c C^c D = M_9 \text{ (minterm 9), etc.}
$$

We utilize this numbering scheme on special Venn diagrams called *minterm maps*. These are illustrated in Figure 1.1 for the cases of three, four, and five generating events. Since the actual content of any minterm depends upon the sets A, B, C, and D in the generating class, it is customary to refer to these sets as *variables*. In the three-variable case, set A is the right half of the diagram and set C is the lower half; set B is split, so that it is the union of the second and fourth columns. Similar splits occur in other cases.

Remark: Other useful arrangements of minterm maps are employed in the analysis of switching circuits. The significance of the minterm partition of the basic space rests in large measure on the following fact.

Minterm Expansion

Each Boolean combination of the sets in a finite generating class may be expressed as the disjoint union of a unique subclass of the minterms. This unique representation is known as the minterm expansion for the combination.

The proposition is made plausible by simple examples utilizing minterm maps to determine graphically the minterm content of various Boolean combinations.

EXAMPLE 1.2
Minterm Expansion

Suppose $E = AB \cup A^c(B \cup C^c)^c$. Examination of the minterm map in Figure 1.2 (p. 8) shows that AB consists of the union of minterms $M6$, $M7$, which we designate $M(6, 7)$. The combination $B \cup C^c = M(0, 2, 3, 4, 6, 7)$, so that its complement $(B \cup C^c)^c = M(1, 5)$. This leaves the common part $A^c(B \cup C^c)^c = M_1$. Hence, $E = M(1, 6, 7)$.

A formal verification of the minterm expansion, utilizing indicator functions, is given in the appendix to this chapter.

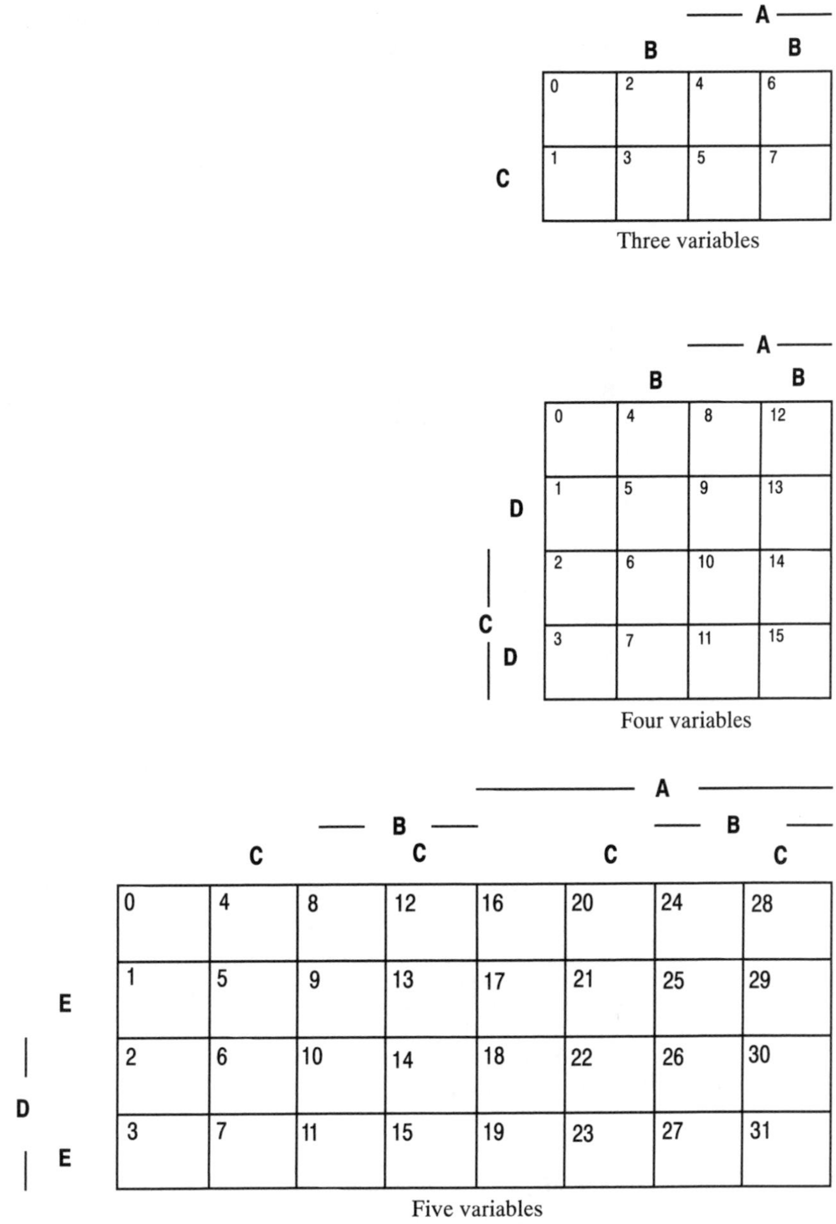

Three variables

	B		B	
C	0	2	4	6
	1	3	5	7

A

Four variables

	B		B	
D	0	4	8	12
	1	5	9	13
C	2	6	10	14
D	3	7	11	15

A

Five variables

C	B C	C	B C
0	4	8	12	16	20	24	28
1	5	9	13	17	21	25	29
2	6	10	14	18	22	26	30
3	7	11	15	19	23	27	31

A

E

D

E

FIGURE 1.1 *Minterm maps for three, four, and five variables*

MINTERM VECTORS

We now examine one of the key concepts in much of the MATLAB implementation developed in this text. Suppose E is a Boolean combination of A, B, C. Then, its minterm expansion is of the form

$$E = \biguplus_{J_E} M_i$$

where M_i is the ith minterm and J_E is the set of indices for those M_i included in E. For example, consider

$$E = A(B \cup C^c) \cup A^c(B \cup C^c)^c = M_1 \uplus M_4 \uplus M_6 \uplus M_7 = M(1,4,6,7)$$
$$F = A^cB^c \cup AC = M_0 \uplus M_1 \uplus M_5 \uplus M_7 = M(0,1,5,7)$$

We may designate each such set by a *unique pattern* of zeros and ones. The ones indicate which minterms are present in the set. For the case of three generating sets, we have eight positions, corresponding to minterms 0 through 7. In the pattern for set E, minterm M_i is included in E iff the entry in position numbered i is 1. This is, in effect, another arrangement of the minterm map. In this form, it is natural to view the pattern as a *minterm vector*, which may be represented by a row matrix of zeros and ones. We find it convenient to use the same symbol for the name of the event and for the minterm vector or matrix representing it. Thus, for the examples above,

$$E \sim [0\ 1\ 0\ 0\ 1\ 0\ 1\ 1] \quad \text{and} \quad F \sim [1\ 1\ 0\ 0\ 0\ 1\ 0\ 1]$$

It should be apparent that this formalization can be extended to sets generated by any finite class.

MINTERM VECTORS FOR BOOLEAN COMBINATIONS

If E and F are combinations of n generating sets, then each is represented by a unique minterm vector of length 2^n. Now Boolean combinations of these are, in effect, Boolean combinations of the generating sets.

1. The minterm expansion for $E \cup F$ has all the minterms in either set. This means the jth element of the vector for $E \cup F$ is the *maximum* of the jth elements for the two vectors.
2. The minterm expansion for $E \cap F$ has only those minterms in both sets. This means the jth element of the vector for $E \cap F$ is the *minimum* of the jth elements for the two vectors.
3. The minterm expansion for E^c has only those minterms not in the expansion for E. This means the vector for E^c has zeros and ones

FIGURE 1.2 *Minterm map representation of minterm expansion*

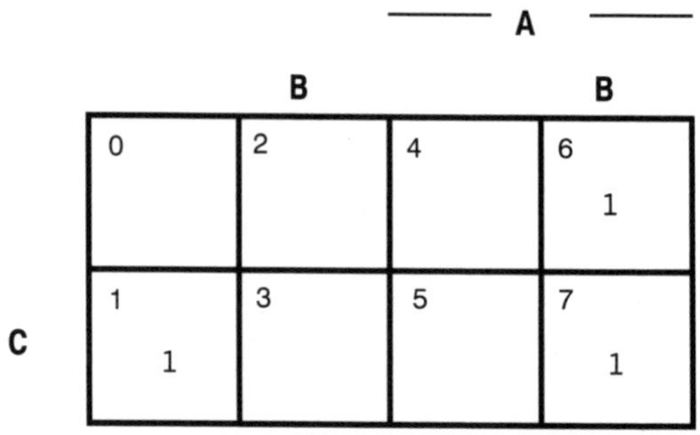

$$E = AB \cup A^c(B \cup C^c)^c = M(1,6,7)$$

interchanged. The jth element of E^c is one iff the corresponding element of E is zero.

We illustrate for the case of the two combinations E and F of three generating sets, considered above:

$$E = A(B \cup C^c) \cup A^c(B \cup C^c)^c \sim [0\ 1\ 0\ 0\ 1\ 0\ 1\ 1] \qquad \text{and}$$

$$F = A^c B^c \cup AC \sim [1\ 1\ 0\ 0\ 0\ 1\ 0\ 1]$$

Then

$$E \cup F \sim [1\ 1\ 0\ 0\ 1\ 1\ 1\ 1], \qquad E \cap F \sim [0\ 1\ 0\ 0\ 0\ 0\ 0\ 1] \qquad \text{and}$$

$$E^c \sim [1\ 0\ 1\ 1\ 0\ 1\ 0\ 0]$$

MATLAB LOGICAL OPERATIONS

Logical operations on zero-one matrices provide a convenient way of handling Boolean combinations of minterm vectors represented as matrices. For two zero-one matrices E, F of the same size

$E\,|\,F$ is the matrix obtained by taking the maximum element in each place.

$E\&F$ is the matrix obtained by taking the minimum element in each place.

$\tilde{}E$ is the matrix obtained by interchanging one and zero in each place in E.

Thus, if E, F are minterm vectors for sets by the same name, then $E\,|\,F$ is the minterm vector for $E \cup F$, $E\&F$ is the minterm vector for $E \cap F$, and $\tilde{}E$ is the minterm vector for E^c.

This suggests a general approach to determining minterm vectors for Boolean combinations. If we start with minterm vectors for the generating sets, we can obtain by MATLAB *logical operations* the minterm vector for any Boolean combination. Suppose, for example, the class of generating sets is $\{A, B, C\}$. Then the minterm vectors for A, B, and C, respectively, are

$$A = [0\ 0\ 0\ 0\ 1\ 1\ 1\ 1]$$
$$B = [0\ 0\ 1\ 1\ 0\ 0\ 1\ 1]$$
$$C = [0\ 1\ 0\ 1\ 0\ 1\ 0\ 1]$$

If $E = AB \cup C^c$, then the logical combination $(A\&B)\,|\,(\tilde{}C)$ of the matrices yields $E = [1\ 0\ 1\ 0\ 1\ 0\ 1\ 1]$.

MATLAB IMPLEMENTATION

Function to Generate Minterm Vectors for a Finite Class

—————————————— MATLAB Script ——————————————

```
function y = minterm(n,k)
% Generates the kth minterm vector in a class of n
% Version of 3/2/93
```

Continues

```
y = [zeros(1,2^(n-k))
   ones(1,2^(n-k))]'*ones(1,2^(k-1));      % Sets basic 0-1 pattern and
                                            % replicates it in columns
y = y(:)';                                  % Stretches y into a single row
```

EXAMPLE 1.3

Minterms for the Class $\{A, B, C\}$

——————————————— MATLAB Script ———————————————

```
>>  A = minterm(3,1)
A  = 0       0       0       0       1       1       1       1
>>  B = minterm(3,2)
B  = 0       0       1       1       0       0       1       1
>>  C = minterm(3,3)
C  = 0       1       0       1       0       1       0       1
```

EXAMPLE 1.4

Minterm Patterns for the Boolean Combinations

$$E = A(B \cup C^c) \cup A^c(B \cup C^c)^c \quad \text{and} \quad F = A^cB^c \cup AC$$

——————————————— MATLAB Script ———————————————

```
>> E = (A&(B|~C))|(~A&(~(B|~C)))
E =  0       1       0       0       1       0       1       1
>> F = (~A&(~B))|(A&C)
F =  1       1       0       0       0       1       0       1
>> E|F =
     1       1       0       0       1       1       1       1
>> E&F =
     0       1       0       0       0       0       0       1
```

Function to Generate a Complete Table of Minterm Vectors Frequently it is desirable to generate the entire table of minterms for a given finite class. Such a function is used as a subroutine in various procedures to be developed later.

——————————————— MATLAB Script ———————————————

```
function y=mintable(n)
% Generates a table of minterm vectors
% Assumes the function minterm
y = zeros(n,2^n);           % Sets the basic matrix
for i = 1:n                 % Determines the rows of mintable
    y(i,:) = minterm(n,i);
end
```

EXAMPLE 1.5

Mintable for Three
Variables

————————————— MATLAB Script —————————————

```
>> M3 = mintable(3)
M3  =  0     0     0     0     1     1     1     1
       0     0     1     1     0     0     1     1
       0     1     0     1     0     1     0     1
```

Minvec Procedures   In procedures based on Boolean combinations of n sets, it is useful to set the minterm vectors for the generating sets and their complements with a procedure *minvecn*. To avoid the awkward handling of E^c in MATLAB as $\tilde{\ }E$, we indicate the complement by Ec instead of $\tilde{\ }E$. For $n = 3$, we have

————————————— MATLAB Script —————————————

```
% file minvec3.m
% Version of 1/2/93
% Sets basic minterm vectors
A = minterm(3,1);
B = minterm(3,2);
C = minterm(3,3);
Ac = ~A;
Bc = ~B;
Cc = ~C;
```

EXAMPLE 1.6

A Boolean
Combination

We wish to generate a matrix whose rows are the minterm vectors for the events $\Omega = A \cup A^c$, A, AB, ABC, C, and $A^c C^c$, respectively.

————————————— MATLAB Script —————————————

```
>> minvec3                            % Sets the basic minterm vectors
>> V = [A|Ac; A; A&B; A&B&C; C; Ac&Cc]; % One Boolean combination on
   each row
>> disp(V)
    1     1     1     1     1     1     1     1  % MATLAB translates
                                                % these into
    0     0     0     0     1     1     1     1  % rows of minterm
                                                % vectors
    0     0     0     0     0     0     1     1
    0     0     0     0     0     0     0     1
    0     1     0     1     0     1     0     1
    1     0     1     0     0     0     0     0
```

Similarly, we may define *minvec4*, *minvec5*, etc.

3. MINTERM PROBABILITIES AND BOOLEAN COMBINATIONS

If we have the probability of every minterm generated by a finite class, we can determine the probability of any Boolean combination of the members of the class. When we know the minterm expansion or, equivalently, the minterm vector, we simply pick out the probabilities corresponding to the minterms in the expansion and add them. We illustrate how this may be done with MATLAB in the following example.

EXAMPLE 1.7
Use of Minterm Probabilities

Consider $E = A(B \cup C^c) \cup A^c(B \cup C^c)^c$ and $F = A^c B^c \cup AC$ of Example 1.6, and suppose the respective minterm probabilities are

$$p_0 = 0.21, \quad p_1 = 0.06, \quad p_2 = 0.29, \quad p_3 = 0.11,$$
$$p_4 = 0.09, \quad p_5 = 0.03, \quad p_6 = 0.14, \quad p_7 = 0.07$$

Use of a minterm map shows $E = M(1, 4, 6, 7)$ and $F = M(0, 1, 5, 7)$, so that

$$P(E) = p_1 + p_4 + p_6 + p_7 = p(1, 4, 6, 7) = 0.36 \quad \text{and}$$
$$P(F) = p(0, 1, 5, 7) = 0.37$$

This is easily handled in MATLAB.

- Use minvec3 to set the generating minterm vectors.
- Use *logical* matrix operations $E = (A\&(B\,|\,Cc))\,|\,(Ac\&(\tilde{}(B\,|\,C)))$ and $F = (Ac\&Bc)\,|\,(A\&C)$ to obtain the minterm vectors for E and F.
- If *pm* is the matrix of minterm probabilities, perform the *algebraic* matrix operations $PE = E * pm'$ and $PF = F * pm'$.

The following is a transcript of the MATLAB procedure.

────────────── MATLAB Script ──────────────

```
>> minvec3
>> E = (A&(B|Cc))|(Ac&~(Bc|Cc));
>> F = (Ac&Bc)|(A&C);
>> pm = 0.01*[21 6 29 11 9 3 14 7];
>> PE = E*pm'
PE  =  0.3600
>> PF = F*pm'
PF  =  0.3700
```

THE FUNDAMENTAL PROBLEM

We seek a MATLAB procedure to solve the fundamental problem. Before attempting this, it may be helpful to examine several examples using minterm maps, in order to understand some of the features of such problems.

EXAMPLE 1.8
Survey on
Software

Let A = the event the person selected has a word processing program, B = the event the person has a spreadsheet program, and C = the event the person has a data base program. Determine all minterms possible as well as $P(A^c BC \uplus AB^c C \uplus ABC^c)$ and $P(A^c B^c C)$.

Solution

The data, expressed in terms of minterm probabilities, are:

$P(A) = p(4, 5, 6, 7) = 0.80$; hence, $P(A^c) = p(0, 1, 2, 3) = 0.20$

$P(B) = p(2, 3, 6, 7) = 0.65$; hence, $P(B^c) = p(0, 1, 4, 5) = 0.35$

$P(C) = p(1, 3, 5, 7) = 0.30$; hence, $P(C^c) = p(0, 2, 4, 6) = 0.70$

$P(ABC) = p(7) = 0.10 \quad P(A^c B^c) = p(0, 1) = 0.05$

$P(AB \cup AC \cup BC) = p(3, 5, 6, 7) = 0.65$

$P(AB^c C) = p(5) = 2p(3) = 2P(A^c BC)$

These data are shown on the minterm map in Figure 1.3 (p. 14). We use the patterns displayed in the minterm map to aid in an algebraic solution for the various minterm probabilities.

$p(2, 3) = p(0, 1, 2, 3) - p(0, 1) = 0.20 - 0.05 = 0.15$

$p(6, 7) = p(2, 3, 6, 7) - p(2, 3) = 0.65 - 0.15 = 0.50$

$p(6) = p(6, 7) - p(7) = 0.50 - 0.10 = 0.40$

$p(3, 5) = p(3, 5, 6, 7) - p(6, 7) = 0.65 - 0.50 = 0.15 \Rightarrow p(3) = 0.05,$
$p(5) = 0.10 \Rightarrow p(2) = 0.10$

$p(1) = p(1, 3, 5, 7) - p(3, 5) - p(7) = 0.30 - 0.15 - 0.10 = 0.05 \Rightarrow$
$p(0) = 0$

$p(4) = p(4, 5, 6, 7) - p(5) - p(6, 7) = 0.80 - 0.10 - 0.50 = 0.20$

Thus, all minterm probabilities are determined. They are displayed in Figure 1.3. From these we get

$$P(A^c BC \uplus AB^c C \uplus ABC^c) = p(3, 5, 6) = 0.05 + 0.10 + 0.40 = 0.55$$
$$\text{and} \quad P(A^c B^c C) = p(1) = 0.05$$

EXAMPLE 1.9
Survey on
Personal
Computers

A survey of 1000 students shows that 565 have PC-compatible desktop computers, 515 have Macintosh desktop computers, and 151 have laptop computers. 51 have all three, 124 have both PC and laptop computers, 212 have at least two of the three, and twice as many own both PC and laptop

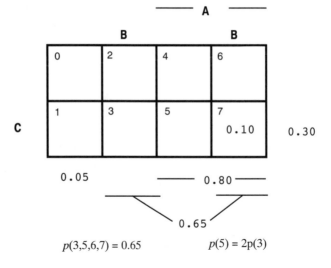

FIGURE 1.3 *Data for software survey. Minterm probabilities for software survey*

computers as those who have both Macintosh desktop and laptop computers. A person is selected at random from this population. What is the probability he or she has at least one of these types of computers? What is the probability the person selected has only a laptop?

Solution

Let A = the event of owning a PC desktop, B = the event of owning a Macintosh desktop, and C = the event of owning a laptop. We utilize a minterm map for three variables to help determine minterm patterns. For example, the event $AC = M_5 \uplus M_7$ so that $P(AC) = p(5) + p(7) = p(5,7)$.

The data, expressed in terms of minterm probabilities, are:

$P(A) = p(4,5,6,7) = 0.565$; hence, $P(A^c) = p(0,1,2,3) = 0.435$

$P(B) = p(2,3,6,7) = 0.515$; hence, $P(B^c) = p(0,1,4,5) = 0.485$

$P(C) = p(1,3,5,7) = 0.151$; hence, $P(C^c) = p(0,2,4,6) = 0.849$

$$P(ABC) = p(7) = 0.051 \qquad P(AC) = p(5,7) = 0.124$$
$$P(AB \cup AC \cup BC) = p(3,5,6,7) = 0.212$$
$$P(AC) = p(5,7) = 2p(3,7) = 2P(BC)$$

We use the patterns displayed in the minterm map to aid in an algebraic solution for the various minterm probabilities.

$$p(5) = p(5,7) - p(7) = 0.124 - 0.051 = 0.073$$
$$p(1,3) = P(A^cC) = 0.151 - 0.124 = 0.027 \quad P(AC^c) = p(4,6) =$$
$$0.565 - 0.124 = 0.441$$
$$p(3,7) = P(BC) = 0.124/2 = 0.062$$
$$p(3) = 0.062 - 0.051 = 0.011$$
$$p(6) = p(3,4,6,7) - p(3) - p(5,7) = 0.212 - 0.011 - 0.124 = 0.077$$
$$p(4) = P(A) - p(6) - p(5,7) = 0.565 - 0.077 - 0.1124 = 0.364$$
$$p(1) = p(1,3) - p(3) = 0.027 - 0.11 = 0.016$$
$$p(2) = P(B) - p(3,7) - p(6) = 0.515 - 0.062 - 0.077 = 0.376$$
$$p(0) = P(C^c) - p(4,6) - p(2) = 0.849 - 0.441 - 0.376 = 0.032$$

We have determined the minterm probabilities, which are displayed on the minterm map in Figure 1.4. We may now compute the probability of any Boolean combination of the generating events A, B, C. Thus,

$$P(A \cup B \cup C) = 1 - P(A^cB^cC^c) = 1 - p(0) = 0.968 \quad \text{and}$$
$$P(A^cB^cC) = p(1) = 0.016$$

The following example exhibits a higher level of complexity. While it can be solved by procedures similar to those used for the previous examples, it illustrates the desirability of a machine procedure which can test for computability of minterm probabilities and of probabilities for the desired Boolean combinations.

FIGURE 1.4 *Minterm probabilities for computer survey*

A		
B		B

C	0	2	4	6
	0.032	0.376	0.364	0.077
	1	3	5	7
	0.016	0.011	0.073	0.051

EXAMPLE 1.10
Opinion Survey

A survey of 1000 persons is made to determine their opinions on four propositions. Let A, B, C, D represent the events that a person selected agrees with the respective propositions. Survey results show the following probabilities for various combinations:

$$A \sim 0.200, \quad B \sim 0.500, \quad C \sim 0.300, \quad D \sim 0.700,$$
$$A(B \cup C^c)D^c \sim 0.055$$

$$A \cup BC \cup D^c \sim 0.520, \quad A^cBC^cD \sim 0.200, \quad ABCD \sim 0.015,$$
$$AB^cC \sim 0.030, \quad A^cB^cC^cD \sim 0.195$$

$$A^cBC \sim 0.120, \quad A^cB^cD^c \sim 0.120, \quad AC^c \sim 0.140,$$
$$ACD^c \sim 0.025, \quad ABC^cD^c \sim 0.020$$

Determine the probabilities for each minterm and for each of the following combinations

$A^c(BC^c \cup B^cC)$—that is, not A and (B or C, but not both)

$A \cup BC^c$—that is, A or (B and not C)

Solution

A step elimination procedure as used in the previous examples shows that all minterms can be calculated. The results are shown on the minterm map in Figure 1.5. However, at the outset it was not clear that the data were consistent or sufficient to determine all minterm probabilities. An examination of the data shows that there are sixteen items (including the fact that the sum of all minterm probabilities is one). Thus, there is hope, but no assurance, that a solution exists. It would be desirable to be able to analyze the problem systematically.

We next consider a simple formal example in which we can compute only one separate minterm probability, yet can compute the desired combination.

EXAMPLE 1.11
Partial Information

Suppose $P(A^c) = 0.4$, $P(AB^c) = 0.4$, and $P(AB(C \cup D^c)) = 0.15$. Determine $P(H) = P(AB^c \cup A(C \cup D^c))$.

Solution

With the aid of a minterm map for four variables A, B, C, D (see Figure 1.6, p. 18), we express the problem in terms of minterm probabilities.

The data are

$$P(A) = 1 - P(A^c) = p(8, 9, 10, 11, 12, 13, 14, 15) = 0.6$$
$$P(AB^c) = p(8, 9, 10, 11) = 0.4 \quad \text{and} \quad P(AB(C \cup D^c)) = p(12, 14, 15) = 0.15$$

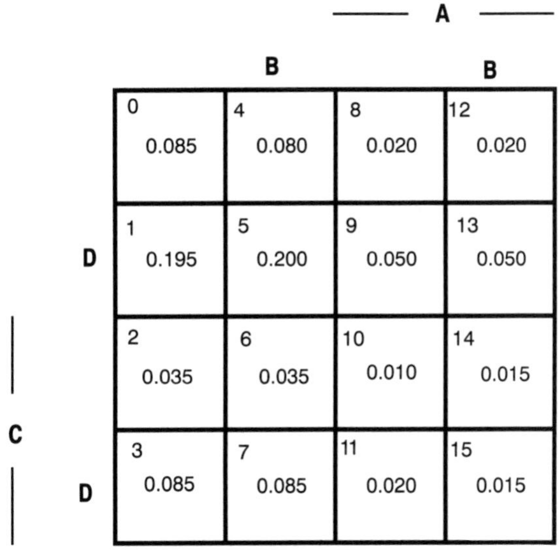
A
B
B
0 0.085
4 0.080
8 0.020
12 0.020
1 0.195
5 0.200
9 0.050
13 0.050
D
2 0.035
6 0.035
10 0.010
14 0.015
C
3 0.085
7 0.085
11 0.020
15 0.015
D

FIGURE 1.5 *Minterm probabilities for opinion survey*

The solution is simply

$$P(H) = P(AB^c \cup A(C \cup D^c)) = p(8, 9, 10, 11, 12, 14, 15)$$
$$= P(AB^c) + p(12, 14, 15) = 0.4 + 0.15 = 0.55$$

As is apparent from the minterm map in Figure 1.6, only minterm probability $p(13)$ is computable.

ORGANIZATION OF THE DATA

We now illustrate the handling of problems of this type with a user-defined procedure *mincalc*. It is necessary to organize the data appropriately for use by mincalc. The data are of the form of a set of equalities

$$P(\text{Boolean combination }) = p$$

We put these *data* into two matrices:

DV—each row is one of the data Boolean combinations

DP—a row matrix; each entry is the probability corresponding to the Boolean combination

The Boolean combinations for which the probabilities are sought are represented as minterm *target vectors* in a matrix TV—one vector on each row.

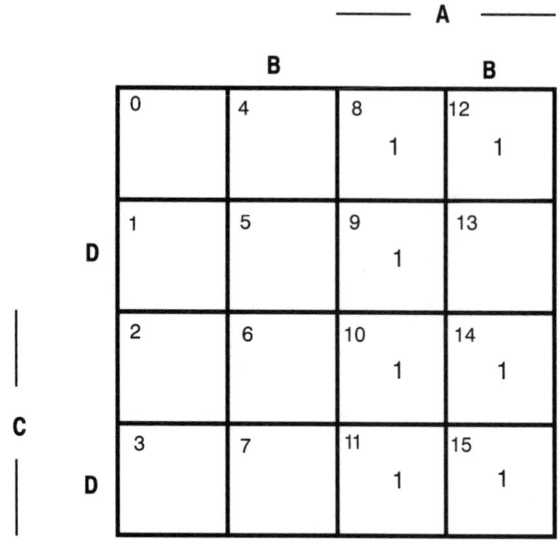

——— A ———

		B		B
	0	4	8 1	12 1
D	1	5	9 1	13
	2	6	10 1	14 1
C D	3	7	11 1	15 1

FIGURE 1.6   *Minterms for problem with partial information*

EXAMPLE 1.8
Survey on Software (Continued)

Consider the introductory example on computer software use. There are three basic events, represented by A, B, C.

- We set the basic minterm vectors by a call for minvec3.
- We represent the data as follows:

Datum	DV entry	DP entry
$P(\Omega) = (P(A \cup A^c) = 1$	A|Ac	1
$P(A) = 0.8$	A	0.8
$P(B) = 0.65$	B	0.65
$P(C) = 0.3$	C	0.3
$P(ABC) = 0.1$	A&B&C	0.1
$P(AB \cup AC \cup BC) = 0.65$	(A&B)|(A&C)|(B&C)	0.65
$P(A^c B^c) = 0.05$	Ac&Bc	0.05

The final datum is in a somewhat different form: $P(AB^c C) = 2P(A^c BC)$. In order to maintain the pattern, we represent this as $P(AB^c C) - 2P(A^c BC) = 0$. The *DV* and *DP* entries are

$$(A\&Bc\&C) - 2 * (Ac\&B\&C) \quad \text{and} \quad 0, \text{ respectively}$$

Note that the parentheses are essential. Within each pair MATLAB performs *logical* operations on zero-one matrices. When these logical combinations are formed, then the linear combination is an *algebraic* operation on the resulting matrices. The data m-file is written as follows:

————————————————— MATLAB Script —————————————————

```
% file mcalc01.m
% The introductory example on software
minvec3;
DV = [A|Ac; A; B; C; A&B&C; (A&B)|(A&C)|(B&C); Ac&Bc; (A&Bc&C)...
  - 2*(Ac&B&C)];
DP = [1 0.8 0.65 0.3 0.1 0.65 0.05 0];
TV = [(A&B&Cc)|(A&Bc&C)|(Ac&B&C); Ac&Bc&C];
disp('Call for mincalc')
```

We now use mincalc to determine the probabilities.

————————————————— MATLAB Script —————————————————

```
>> mcalc01
Call for mincalc
>> mincalc
Data vectors are linearly independent
 Computable target probabilities
     1.0000     0.5500
     2.0000     0.0500
The number of minterms is 8
The number of available minterms is 8
Available minterm probabilities are in vector pma
To view available minterm probabilities, call for PMA
>> disp(PMA)                % Optional call for minterm probabilities
         0          0
    1.0000     0.0500
    2.0000     0.1000
    3.0000     0.0500
    4.0000     0.2000
    5.0000     0.1000
    6.0000     0.4000
    7.0000     0.1000
```

It is apparent that the solution agrees with the results determined by the use of the minterm map and algebraic combinations.

EXAMPLE 1.9

PC Survey
(Continued)

————————————————— MATLAB Script —————————————————

```
% file mcalc02.m
% Personal computer example
minvec3
```

Continues

```
DV =    [A|Ac; A; B; C; A&B&C; A&C; (A&B)|(A&C)|(B&C);...
    2*(B&C) - (A&C)];
DP = 0.001*[1000 565 515 151 51 124 212 0];
TV = [A|B|C; Ac&Bc&C];
disp('Call for mincalc')
>> mcalc02
Call for mincalc
>> mincalc
Data vectors are linearly independent
 Computable target probabilities
    1.0000    0.9680
    2.0000    0.0160
The number of minterms is 8
The number of available minterms is 8
Available minterm probabilities are in vector pma
To view available minterm probabilities, call for PMA

>> disp(PMA)              % Optional call for minterm
                             probabilities

         0    0.032
    1.0000    0.0160
    2.0000    0.3760
    3.0000    0.0110
    4.0000    0.3640
    5.0000    0.0730
    6.0000    0.0770
    7.0000    0.0510
```

EXAMPLE 1.10

Opinion Survey
(Continued)

_____ MATLAB Script _____

```
% file mcalc03.m
% Opinion survey example
minvec4
DV = [A|Ac; A; B; C; D; A&(B|Cc)&Dc; A|((B&C)|Dc) ;
    Ac&B&Cc&D; ...
        A&B&C&D; A&Bc&C; Ac&Bc&Cc&D; Ac&B&C; Ac&Bc&Dc;
        A&Cc;A&C&Dc; A&B&Cc&Dc];
DP =   0.001*[1000 200 500 300 700 55 520 200 15 30 195...
            120 120 140 25 20];
TV = [Ac&((B&Cc)|(Bc&C)); A|(B&Cc)];
disp('Call for mincalc')
>> mcalc03
Call for mincalc
```

Continues

```
>> mincalc
Data vectors are linearly independent
 Computable target probabilities
      1.0000    0.4000
      2.0000    0.4800
The number of minterms in 16
The number of available minterms is 16
Available minterm probabilities are in vector pma
To view available minterm probabilities, call for PMA
```

There are sixteen minterm probabilities. To display these requires 17 lines, including the call line. It would often be useful, as well as space saving, to display these in the format of a minterm map. The following user-defined MATLAB function achieves this arrangement.

_____ MATLAB Script _____

```
function y = minmap(pm)
% pm a row (or column) matrix of minterm probabilities
% Reshapes into minterm map format
% Version of 12/9/93
m = length(pm);
n = round(log(m)/log(2));
a = fix(n/2);
if m ~= 2^n
  disp('The number of minterms is incorrect')
else
  y = reshape(pm,2^a,2^(n-a));
end
```

We use this on the previous example to get a display of the minterm probabilities.

_____ MATLAB Script _____

```
>> p = minmap(pma)
p =
      0.0850    0.0800    0.0200    0.0200
      0.1950    0.2000    0.0500    0.0500
      0.0350    0.0350    0.0100    0.0150
      0.0850    0.0850    0.0200    0.0150
```

In each of these examples, the data are consistent and sufficient for computing all the minterm probabilities (and hence the probability of any Boolean combination). The next example illustrates a situation in which partial information is sufficient to calculate the probability of the specified Boolean combination, although only one individual minterm probability is available.

EXAMPLE 1.12 ——————————— MATLAB Script ———————————

Partial Information
```
% file mcalc04.m
% Partial information
minvec4
DV = [A|Ac; Ac; A&Bc; A&B&(C|Dc)];
DP = [1 0.4 0.4 0.15];
TV = (A&Bc)|(A&(C|Dc));
disp('Call for mincalc')
>> mcalc04
Call for mincalc
>> mincalc
Data vectors are linearly independent
 Computable target probabilities
     1.0000    0.5500
The number of minterms is 16
The number of available minterms is 1
Available minterm probabilities are in vector pma
To view available minterm probabilities, call for PMA
>> PMA
PMA = 13.0000    0.0500
```

For examples illustrating other possibilities, see the Exploration Problems at the end of the chapter.

THE PROCEDURE MINCALC

If we have the probabilities of a suitable set of Boolean combinations, we may solve algebraically for the minterm probabilities and/or for the probabilities of other "target" Boolean combinations. In the solutions of the previous examples, we utilize a combination of logical methods using minterm maps and an algebraic treatment using representations of the minterm expansion. With the aid of a very simple example, we reformulate the solution procedure in a manner that can be implemented in terms of MATLAB operations.

EXAMPLE 1.13
A Solution Procedure for MATLAB Implementation

Given the following data: $P(A(B \cup C)) = 0.3$, $P(A^c) = 0.6$, and $P(A^c B^c C^c) = 0.1$, determine $P(B \cup C)$. Note that we always have the information $P(\Omega) = $ the sum of all minterm probabilities $= 1$. Reference to a minterm map for three variables shows that

$$P1 = P(\Omega) = P(A \cup A^c) = p(0,1,2,3,4,5,6,7) = 1$$
$$P2 = P(A(B \cup C))) = p(5,6,7) = 0.3$$
$$P3 = P(A^c) = p(0,1,2,3) = 0.6$$
$$P4 = p(0) = 0.1$$

Use of the minterm map and simple algebra shows

$$P = P(B \cup C) = p(1,2,3,5,6,7) = P2 + P3 - P4 = 0.8$$

We can express the data and the solution in terms of minterm vectors and appropriate probability vectors. If pm is the vector of minterm probabilities, then

$P1 = v_1 * pm'$ where $v_1 = [1\ 1\ 1\ 1\ 1\ 1\ 1\ 1]$
$P2 = v_2 * pm'$ where $v_2 = [0\ 0\ 0\ 0\ 0\ 1\ 1\ 1]$
$P3 = v_3 * pm'$ where $v_3 = [1\ 1\ 1\ 1\ 0\ 0\ 0\ 0]$
$P4 = v_4 * pm'$ where $v_4 = [1\ 0\ 0\ 0\ 0\ 0\ 0\ 0]$
$P\ \ = v * pm'$ where $v = B|C = [0\ 1\ 1\ 1\ 0\ 1\ 1\ 1]$

Now a careful examination and use of elementary properties of matrices show that

$$v = v_2 + v_3 - v_4 \quad \text{and}$$
$$P = v * pm' = v_2 * pm' + v_3 * pm' - v_4 * pm' = P2 + P3 - P4$$

The solution amounts to this: given the minterm vectors v_1, v_2, v_3, v_4, we can determine v as a linear combination of these vectors. Then P is the *same linear combination* of $P1 = 1, P2, P3, P4$.

We illustrate with a MATLAB formulation.

- We set the basic minterm vectors with minvec3.
- We use *logical operations* on the basic minterm vectors for A, B, and C to produce the minterm vectors v_1, v_2, v_3, v_4 for the data combinations.
- We determine a linear combination $c_1 v_1 + c_2 v_2 + c_3 v_3 + c_4 v_4$ which is equal to the "target" minterm vector v.
- The probability of the target combination is $c_1 P_1 + c_2 P_2 + c_3 P_3 + c_4 P_4$.

Note that we determine the minterm vectors v_1, v_2, v_3, v_4 by *logical* operations, then determine an *algebraic* combination of these to yield v.

─────────────────────── MATLAB Script ───────────────────────

```
>> minvec3              % Set basic minterm vectors
>> v1 = A|Ac;           % Use of logical operations to
                        % determine data vectors
>> v2 = A&(B|C);
>> v3 = Ac;
>> v4 = Ac&Bc&Cc;
>> p1 = 1;              % Enter the data probabilities
>> p2 = 0.3;
>> p3 = 0.6;
>> p4 = 0.1;
>> v  = B|C;
>> disp(v)
     0   1   1   1   0   1   1   1    % Determined by logical operations
>> disp(v2 + v3 - v4)
     0   1   1   1   0   1   1   1    % Determined by algebraic operations
>> P = p2 + p3 - p4
P  =  0.8000
```

The principal remaining question is: if $v = c_1 v_1 + c_2 v_2 + c_3 v_3 + c_4 v_4$, can MATLAB determine the coefficients of the linear combination? The answer is yes. Here we use *algebraic* operations, including a special method for solving under- or over-determined equations.

─────────────────────── MATLAB Script ───────────────────────

```
>> DV = [v1; v2; v3; v4];   % Matrix whose rows are the data vectors
>> DP = [p1 p2 p3 p4]       % Matrix of the data probabilities
>> C = v/DV                 % Matrix of the coefficients
C = -0.0000 1.0000 1.0000 -1.0000 % -0.0000 is an oddity of MATLAB
                            % subtraction
>> P = C*DP'
P = 0.8000
```

It should be apparent that the operations in this simple example extend to larger and more general problems. The essential strategy and process remain the same, although the details become much more complex. We summarize as follows.

BASIS FOR THE PROCEDURE MINCALC

- Use the MATLAB procedure minvecq to set minterm vectors for each of q basic events. Let $n_d = 2^q$. Each minterm vector is a $(1 \times n_d)$ row vector of zeros and ones.
- MATLAB translates any Boolean combination of the basic vectors into another $(1 \times n_d)$ minterm vector.
- *Data* consist of m_d Boolean combinations of the basic vectors and their respective probabilities. These are organized into two matrices:

1. The *data vector matrix DV* has the m_d data Boolean combinations—one on each row. MATLAB translates this into a $(m_d \times n_d)$ vector of zeros and ones; each row is the minterm vector for the corresponding Boolean combination. The first entry (on the first row) is $A \uplus A^c$, which is the whole space. The minterm vector consists of a row of n_d ones.
2. The *data probability matrix DP* is a $(1 \times m_d)$ matrix of the data probabilities. The first entry is one, the probability of the whole space (expressed as $A \uplus A^c$).

- For the *target* Boolean combinations, there are m_t such combinations whose probabilities are sought. These are put into the *target vector matrix TV*, one on each row. MATLAB produces an $(m_t \times n_d)$ matrix of zeros and ones. Each row is the minterm vector for the corresponding Boolean combination.

Usual case   Suppose the data minterm vectors are linearly independent and the target vectors are each linearly dependent on the data minterm vectors. Then each target minterm vector is expressible as a linear combination of data minterm vectors. Thus, there is a $(m_t \times m_d)$ matrix CT such that

$$TV = CT * DV \qquad (m_t \times n_d) \leftrightarrow (m_t \times m_d)(m_d \times n_d)$$

MATLAB solves this with the command $CT = TV/DV$. As the preceding argument shows, *the target probabilities are the same linear combinations of the data probabilities*. These are obtained by the MATLAB operation

$$tp = DP * CT' \qquad (1 \times m_t) \leftrightarrow (1 \times m_d)(m_d \times m_t)$$

The *refinements* in the procedure consist of determining consistency of the data probabilities and the computability of various individual minterm probabilities and target probabilities. The consistency check is principally for negative minterm probabilities. The computability tests are tests for linear dependence by means of calculation of ranks of the relevant matrices. The procedure picks out the computable minterm probabilities and the computable target probabilities and calculates them.

Cautionary notes: The program mincalc depends upon the provision in MATLAB for solving equations when less than full data are available. There are several situations which should be dealt with as special cases.

1. **The Zero Problem.** If the total probability of a group of minterms is zero, then it follows that the probability of each minterm in the group is zero. However, if mincalc does not have enough information to calculate the separate minterm probabilities in the case they are not zero, it will not pick up in the zero case that the separate minterm probabilities are zero. It simply considers these minterm probabilities not computable. See the Exploration Problem P1.4 on the "zero problem."

2. **Linear dependence.** In the case of linear dependence, the operation called for by the command CT = TV/DV may not be able to solve the equations. The matrix may be singular, or it may not be able to decide which of the redundant data equations to use. Should it provide a solution, the result should be checked with the aid of a minterm map.

3. **Consistency check.** Since the consistency check is for negative minterms, if there are not enough data to calculate the minterm probabilities, there is no simple check on the consistency. Sometimes the probability of a target vector included in another vector will actually exceed what should be the larger probability. Without considerable checking, it may be difficult to determine consistency.

4. In a few unusual cases, the command CT = TV/DV does not operate appropriately, even though the data should be adequate for the problem at hand. Apparently the approximation process does not converge. This problem has been observed on a personal computer, although the same problem is solved without difficulty on a Unix workstation. The difficulty may lie in the reduced precision of representation of numbers in the personal computer.

_____ MATLAB Script _____

```
% file mincalc.m
% Version of 12/12/93
% Assumes a data file which includes
%   1. Call for minvecq to set q basic minterm vectors, each (1 x 2^q)
%   2. Data vectors DV = matrix of md data Boolean combinations of
%        basic sets—
%      MATLAB produces md minterm vectors— one on each row.
%      The first combination is always A|Ac (the whole space)
%   3. DP = row matrix of md data probabilities.
%      The first probability is always 1.
%   4. Target vectors TV = matrix of mt target Boolean combinations.
%      MATLAB produces a row minterm vector for each target combination.
%      If there are no target combinations, set TV - [];
[md,nd] = size(DV);
ND = 0:nd-1;
```

Continues

```
ID = eye(nd);                      % Row i is minterm vector i-1
[mt,nt] = size(TV);
MT = 1:mt;
rd = rank(DV);
if rd < md                         % End is on last computational line
   disp('Data vectors are NOT linearly independent')
   else
   disp('Data vectors are linearly independent')
% Identification of which minterm probabilities can be determined from the data
% (i.e., which minterm vectors are not linearly independent of data vectors)
AM = zeros(1,nd);
for i = i:nd
   AM(i) = rd == rank([DV;ID(i,:)]);   % Checks for linear dependence of each
   end                                  % minterm vector
CAM = ID(AM,;)/DV;                 % Determination of coefficients for the
                                   % available minterms
pma = DP*CAM';                     % Calculation of probabilities of
                                   % available
                                   % minterms
PMA = [ND(AM);pma]';
if sum(pma < -0.001) > 0           % Check for data consistency
   disp('Data probabilities are INCONSISTENT')
else
% Identification of which target probabilities are computable from the data
CT = zeros(1,mt);
for j = 1:mt
   CT(j) = rd == rank([DV;TV(j,:)]);
   end
CCT = TV(CT,:)/DV;                 % Determination of coefficients for computable
                                   % targets
ctp = DP*CCT';                     % Determination of probabilities
disp(' Computable target probabilities')
disp([MT(CT); ctp]')
end                                % end for "if sum(pma < -0.001) > 0"
end                                % end for "if rd < md"
disp(['The number of minterms is ',num2str(nd),])
disp(['The number of available minterms is ',num2str(length(pma)),])
disp('Available minterm probabilities are in vector pma')
disp('To view available minterm probabilities, call for PMA')
```

THE PROCEDURE MINCALCT

Various modifications of this procedure may be desirable. For example, it might be desirable to have the procedure prompt for inputs. Then, if the data vector matrix, etc. had different symbols, these could be used. One useful modification, which we call *mincalct*, computes the available target probabilities without checking and computing the minterm probabilities. This procedure assumes a data file similar to that for mincalc except that it does not need the target matrix *TV*, since it prompts for target Boolean combination inputs. The procedure mincalct may be used after mincalc has performed its operations to calculate probabilities for additional target combinations.

—————————————— MATLAB Script ——————————————

```
% file mincalct.m
% Version of 9/1/93
% Assumes a data file which includes
%   1. Call for minvecq to set q basic minterm vectors.
%   2. Data vectors DV. The first combination is always A|Ac.
%   3. Row matrix DP data probabilities. The first entry is always 1.
TV = input('Enter matrix of target Boolean combinations ');
[md,nd] = size(DV);
[mt,nt] = size(TV);
MT = 1:mt;
rd = rank(DV);
CT = zeros(1,mt);    % Identification of computable target probabilities
for j = 1:mt
  CT(j) = rd == rank([DV;TV(j,:)]);
end
CCT = TV(CT,:)/DV;   % Determination of coefficients for computable targets
ctp = DP*CCT';       % Determination of probabilities
disp(' Computable target probabilities')
disp([MT(CT); ctp]')
disp(' ')
```

——

● ———————

EXAMPLE 1.14
An Additional
Target Probability

Suppose mincalct has been applied to the data for the opinion survey and that it is desired to determine $P(AD \cup BD^c)$. It is not necessary to recalculate all the other quantities. We may simply use the procedure mincalct and input the desired Boolean combination at the prompt.

—————————————— MATLAB Script ——————————————

```
>> mincalct
Enter matrix of target Boolean combinations (A&D)|(B&Dc)
 Computable target probabilities
     1.0000    0.2850
```

——

Repeated calls for mcalct may be used to compute other target probabilities.

——————————— ●

SUMMARY

The functions and procedures based on the minterm vector concept provide tools for systematic handling of Boolean combinations of a finite number of events. These functions combine with MATLAB algebraic techniques to provide powerful tools for dealing with the fundamental problem: given the probabilities of certain Boolean combinations of events, find the probabilities of others. Although the procedure mincalc is not completely foolproof, if appropriate data are supplied, the desired probabilities are calculated easily. In many cases the program can find inconsistencies or linear dependencies and provide suitable warnings.

4. APPENDIX. THE INDICATOR FUNCTION FOR A SET

Two concepts play a fundamental role in the methodology we employ:

1. The *minterm expansion,* in the analysis of Boolean combinations of events.
2. The *indicator function,* in the representation and analysis of simple random variables (i.e., those having a finite set of possible values).

The roles of these two concepts are intimately related. The minterm expansion is introduced informally in Section 2. We next introduce the indicator function, note some of its properties, and use it to examine more formally the minterm expansion.

The *indicator function* I_E on Ω for a subset E is defined by

$$I_E(\omega) = \begin{cases} 1 & \text{for } \omega \in E \\ 0 & \text{otherwise} \end{cases}$$

The properties of this function are well known (cf. *PA*, Sections 1.3 and 1.4).

1. $A \subset B$ iff $I_A(\omega) \leq I_B(\omega)$ for all ω.
2. $A = B$ iff $I_A(\omega) = I_B(\omega)$ for all ω.
3. If $E = \bigcup_{i=1}^{n} E_i$, then $I_E = \max\{I_{E_i} : 1 \leq i \leq n\}$.

   If $E = \biguplus_{i=1}^{n} E_i$ (disjoint union), then $I_E = \sum_{i=1}^{n} I_{E_i}$ (the class $\{E_i : 1 \leq i \leq n\}$ is disjoint).

   If $E = \bigcap_{i=1}^{n} E_i$, then $I_E = \min\{I_{E_i} : 1 \leq i \leq n\}$.

   Also, $I_{E^c} = 1 - I_E$.

A number of further facts essential to our analysis follow from these elementary properties. These provide a validation of the minterm expansion and lay the basis for an analysis of simple random variables.

1. The indicator function for a Boolean combination is a numerical valued function of the indicator functions for the individual sets. As an indicator function, it takes on only the values zero and one.

2. The value of the indicator function for each generating set must be constant on each minterm; hence, the value of the indicator function for any Boolean combination must be constant on each minterm. For example, for each ω in the minterm AB^cCD^c, we must have $I_A(\omega) = 1$, $I_B(\omega) = 0$, $I_C(\omega) = 1$, and $I_D(\omega) = 0$. Thus, any function of I_A, I_B, I_C, I_D must be constant over the minterm. This fact plays an essential role in the analysis of simple random variables in Chapter 4.

3. Consider a Boolean combination E of generating sets. Let the subclass of those minterms on which I_E has the value one be $\{M_i : i \in J_E\}$. Let $F = \underset{J_E}{\biguplus} M_i$. Since the minterms are disjoint (mutually exclusive), we have

$$I_F = \sum_{J_E} I_{M_i}$$

This ensures that $I_F(\omega)$ has value one on each minterm M_i in the subclass and has value zero on each minterm outside the class. Thus, $I_F(\omega) = I_E(\omega)$ for all ω, so that $E = F$. This establishes the minterm expansion.

The minterm vector for E may be viewed as a display of the values which the indicator function I_E has on each minterm. This implies that minterm vectors for Boolean combinations of sets are obtained by simple rules, which are alternate manifestations of the rules for the underlying indicator functions. Thus, minterm vectors for Boolean combinations are obtained by the following rules.

1. The jth element of the vector for $\bigcup_{i=1}^{n} E_i$ is the *maximum* of the jth elements for each of the E_i.

2. The jth element of the vector for $\bigcap_{i=1}^{n} E_i$ is the *minimum* of the jth elements for each of the E_i.

3. The jth element of the vector for E^c is one minus the jth element of the vector for E. This results in the interchange of zeros and ones.

As we note in the development of the procedure mincalc, above, these properties make it possible for MATLAB to handle minterm vectors for Boolean combinations.

REINFORCEMENT EXERCISES AND EXPLORATION PROBLEMS

■

REINFORCEMENT EXERCISES

P1.1 Which of the following statements are true?

   a. $[A \cup (BC)^c]^c = (A \cup B)^c (B \cup C)$

   b. $A \subset AC \cup (A^c \cup B^c C)^c \cup A^c B^c C$

   c. $(A \cup B)^c = A^c C \cup B^c C$

   d. $ABC \subset AB \cup BC \cup AC$

   Suggestion: Use minvec3 to simplify writing. Check results with minterm map.

P1.2 Use the data in the following m-file with mincalc.

―――――――――――――――― MATLAB Script ――――――――――――――――

```
minvec4
DV = [A|Ac; A; B; C; D; (A&B)|(Cc&Dc); ((A&Bc)|Ac)&C; Ac&Cc&D;
A&B&Cc&D];
DP = [1 0.3360 0.5500 0.6820 0.5360 0.3210 0.6050 0.0660...
0.0590];
TV = [(Ac&C)|((A&Bc)&(C|D))];
disp('Call for mincalc')
```

P1.3 Use the data in the following m-file with mincalc.

―――――――――――――――― MATLAB Script ――――――――――――――――

```
minvec4
DV = [A|Ac; A; B; C; D; (A&B)|(Cc&Dc); ((A&Bc)|Ac)&C; Ac&Cc&D;
A&B&Cc&D; A&Bc&C&D; Ac&Bc&C&D; Ac&C&Dc; Ac&B&C; Ac&B&Dc;
Ac&Bc&Cc];
DP = [1.000 0.336 0.550 0.680 0.536 0.321 0.605 0.066 0.059...
0.104 0.105 0.185 0.209 0.225 0.041];
TV = [(Ac&(B|C))|(A&Bc&D); (C&Dc)|(Cc&D); Ac&Cc ];
disp('Call for mincalc')
```

P1.4 Use the data in the following m-file with mincalc.

```
minvec4
DV = [A|Ac; A; B; C; D; (A&B)|(Cc&Dc); ((A&Bc)|Ac)&C; Ac&Cc&D;
A&B&Cc&D; A&Bc&C&D; Ac&Bc&C&D; Ac&C&Dc; Ac&B&C; Ac&B&Dc;
Ac&Bc&Cc; A&Bc ];
DP = [1.000 0.336 0.550 0.680 0.536 0.321 0.605 0.066 0.059...
0.104 0.105 0.185 0.209 0.225 0.041 0.199];
TV = [(Ac&(B|C))|(A&Bc&D); (C&Dc)|(Cc&D); Ac&Cc ];
disp('Call for mincalc')
```

P1.5 Suppose $P(A \cup B^c C) = 0.65$, $P(AC) = 0.2$, $P(A^c B) = 0.25$, $P(A^c C^c) = 0.25$, $P(BC^c) = 0.30$.

Determine $P((AC^c \cup A^c C)B^c)$ $P((AB^c \cup A^c)C^c)$ and $P(A^c(B \cup C^c))$, if possible.

P1.6 Suppose $P((AB^c \cup A^c B)C) = 0.4$, $P(AB) = 0.2$, $P(A^c C^c) = 0.3$, $P(A) = 0.6$, $P(C) = 0.5$, and $P(AB^c C^c) = 0.1$.

Determine $P(A^c C^c \cup AC)$ $P((AB^c \cup A^c)C^c)$ and $P(A^c(B \cup C^c))$, if possible.

P1.7 Suppose $P(A(B \cup C)) = 0.3$, $P(A^c) = 0.6$, and $P(A^c B^c C^c) = 0.1$.

Determine $P(B \cup C)$ $P((AB \cup A^c B^c)C^c \cup AC)$ and $P(A^c(B \cup C^c))$, if possible.

Repeat the problem with the additional data $P(A^c BC) = 0.2$ and $P(A^c B) = 0.3$.

P1.8 Suppose $P(A) = 0.6$, $P(C) = 0.4$, $P(AC) = 0.3$, $P(A^c B) = 0.2$, and $P(A^c B^c C^c) = 0.1$.

Determine $P((A \cup B)C^c)$ $P(AC^c \cup A^c C)$ and $P(AC^c \cup A^c B)$, if possible.

P1.9 Suppose $P(A) = 0.5$, $P(AB) = P(AC) = 0.3$, and $P(ABC^c) = 0.1$.

Determine $P(A(BC^c)^c)$ and $P(AB \cup AC \cup BC)$. Then repeat with additional data $P(A^c B^c C^c) = 0.1$ and $P(A^c BC) = 0.05$. What is the result?

P1.10 Given the following data,

$$P(A) = 0.55, \ P(AB) = 0.30, \ P(BC) = 0.20, \ P(A^c \cup BC) = 0.55, \ P(A^c BC^c) = 0.15$$

determine, if possible, $P(A^c \,|\, B) = P(A^c B)/P(B)$.

P1.11 Consider the class $\{A, B, C, D\}$ of events. Suppose the probability that at least one of the events A or C occurs is 0.75 and the probability that at least one of the four events occurs is 0.90.

Determine the probability that neither events A or C occurs but at least one of the events B or D occurs.

P1.12 A survey of 1000 persons is made to determine their opinions on four propositions. Let A, B, C, and D be the events a person agrees with the respective propositions. Survey results show the following probabilities for various combinations:

$A \sim 0.200, \ B \sim 0.500, \ C \sim 0.300, \ D \sim 0.700,$

$A(B \cup C^c)D^c \sim 0.051$, $A \cup BC \cup D^c \sim 0.524$,
$A^c BC^c D \sim 0.196$, $ABCD \sim 0.021$, $AB^c C \sim 0.030$,
$A^c B^c C^c D \sim 0.196$, $A^c BC \sim 0.119$, $A^c B^c D^c \sim 0.120$,
$AC^c \sim 0.139$, $ACD^c \sim 0.019$, $ABC^c D^c \sim 0.020$

Determine the probabilities for each minterm and for each of the following combinations:

$$AD(BC)^c \cup A^c BC^c \cup B^c CD \quad \text{and} \quad A^c BC^c \cup ABC$$

P1.13 A survey of 100 students yields the following information:

> 52 percent are male
> 85 percent live on campus
> 78 percent are male or are active in intramural sports (or both)
> 30 percent live on campus but are not active in sports
> 32 percent are male, live on campus, and are active in sports
> 41 percent are females active in intramural sports
> 17 percent are male student inactive in sports

> a. What is the probability that a student picked at random is male and lives on campus?
> b. What is the probability of a male on-campus student who is not active in sports?
> c. What is the probability of a female student active in sports?

P1.14 A survey of 100 persons of voting age reveals that 60 are male, 30 of whom do not identify with a political party; 50 are members of a political party; 20 are nonmembers of a party voted in the last election, 10 of whom are female. How many nonmembers of a political party did not vote? *Suggestion:* express the numbers as a fraction, and treat as probabilities.

P1.15 One hundred students are questioned about their courses of study and plans for graduate study. Let A = the event the student is male; B = the event the student is studying engineering; C = the event the student plans at least one year of foreign language; D = the event the student is planning graduate study (including professional school). The results of the survey are:

There are 55 men students— $P(A) = 0.55$
There are 23 engineering students, 10 of whom are women—
$P(B) = 0.23$, $P(A^c B) = 0.10$
75 students will take foreign language classes, including all women—
$P(C) = 0.75$, $P(A^c C^c) = 0$
26 men and 19 women plan graduate study—
$P(AD) = 26$, $P(A^c D) = 0.19$
13 male engineering students and 8 women engineering students plan graduate study—
$P(ABD) = 0.13$, $P(A^c BD) = 0.08$
20 engineering students will take a foreign language and plan graduate

study—

$P(BCD) = 0.20$

5 nonengineering students plan graduate study but no foreign language courses—

$P(B^c C^c D) = 0.05$

11 nonengineering female students plan foreign language study and graduate study—

$P(A^c B^c CD) = 0.11$

a. What is the probability a student selected at random plans foreign language classes and graduate study?

b. What is the probability of a female engineer who does not plan graduate study?

c. What is the probability of a male student who either studies a foreign language but does not intend graduate study or will not study a foreign language but plans graduate study?

Suppose there is an additional item of data: $P(ACD) = 0.20$. Recalculate the problem.

P1.16 A survey of 100 students shows that:

60 are male students

55 students live on campus, 25 of whom are women

40 read the student newspaper regularly, 25 of whom are women

70 consider themselves reasonably active in student affairs; 50 of these live on campus

35 of the reasonably active students read the newspaper regularly

All women who live on campus and 5 who live off campus consider themselves to be active

10 of the on-campus female readers consider themselves active, as do 5 of the off-campus women

5 men are active, off-campus, and nonreaders of the newspaper

a. How many active men are either not readers or live off campus?

b. How many inactive men are not regular readers?

P1.17 A television station runs a telephone survey to determine how many persons in its primary viewing area have watched three recent special programs, which we call a, b, and c. Of the 1000 persons surveyed, the results are:

221 have seen program a

209 have seen program b

112 have seen program c

197 have seen at least two of the programs

45 have seen all three

62 have seen at least a and c

The number having seen at both a and b is twice as large as the number who have seen at both b and c.

a. How many have seen at least one special?

b. How many have seen only one special program?

P1.18 An automobile safety inspection station found that in 1000 cars tested:

100 needed wheel alignment, brake repair, and headlight adjustment

325 needed at least two of these three items

125 needed headlight and brake work

550 needed wheel alignment

a. How many needed only wheel alignment?

b. How many who did not need wheel alignment needed one or none of the other items?

P1.19 A survey of 1000 persons is made to determine their opinions on four propositions. Let A, B, C, and D be the events a person agrees with the respective propositions. Survey results show the following probabilities for various combinations:

$A \sim 0.200$, $B \sim 0.500$, $C \sim 0.300$, $D \sim 0.700$,

$A(B \cup C^c)D^c \sim 0.055$, $A \cup BC \cup D^c \sim 0.520$,

$A^cBC^cD \sim 0.200$, $ABCD \sim 0.015$, $AB^cC \sim 0.030$,

$A^cB^cC^cD \sim 0.195$, $A^cBC \sim 0.120$, $A^cB^cD \sim 0.120$,

$AC^c \sim 0.140$, $ACD^c \sim 0.025$, $ABC^cD^c \sim 0.020$

Determine the probabilities for each minterm and for each of the following combinations:

a. $A^c(BC^c \cup B^cC)$—that is, not A and (B or C, but not both).

b. $A \cup BC^c$—that is, A or (B and not C).

P1.20 Given $P(A) = 0.6$, $P(A^cB^c) = 0.2$, $P(AC^c) = 0.4$, and $P(ACD^c) = 0.1$, determine $P(A^cB \cup A(C^c \cup D))$.

EXPLORATION PROBLEMS

P1.1 Data are: $P(A) = 0.4$, $P(AB) = 0.3$, $P(ABC) = 0.25$, $P(C) = 0.65$, $P(A^cC^c) = 0.3$. Determine available minterm probabilities and the following, if computable:

$$P(AC^c \cup A^cC), \quad P(A^cB^c), \quad P(A \cup B), \quad P(AB^c)$$

How many items of data are needed to calculate all minterms. Use a minterm map or display of the data vectors to find suitable items. Try the following additional data: $P(A^cBC^c) = 0.1$ and $P(A^cB^c) = 0.3$

P1.2 Suppose in the original problem $P(AB)$ is changed from 0.3 to 0.5. What is the result? Explain. What are the calculated minterm probabilities?

P1.3 Suppose the problem has the original data probability matrix but in the data vector matrix $A\&B$ is replaced by $A\&C$. What is the new result? Does mincalc still work in this case? Check the results on a minterm map.

P1.4 **The zero problem** To see the behavior of mincalc with respect to groups of minterms with zero probability, consider the following data file:

minvec3

DV = [A-Ac; A; B; Ac&B; Ac&B&C; A&C];

DP = [1 0.7 0.8 0.3 0.2 0.2];

TV = [Ac&Bc]; % Minterms 0, 1

Call for mincalc

What is the probability of $A^c B^c$? Does mincalc separate the probabilities for minterms 0, 1? Enter the data onto a minterm map. What does this show? Modify the data probability matrix to

DP = [1 0.6 0.6 0.2 0.1 0.2];

What does this do to the probability distribution on the minterm map? Call for mincalc again. Does it separate the probabilities for minterms 0, 1? Augment the matrix DV by entering Ac&Bc&C as a last row, and augment the modified DP with a corresponding probability 0.1 in the corresponding position. Call for mincalc. Are probabilities for minterms 0, 1 calculated?

Now use the augmented data matrix DV, and modify the *original DP* by putting 0 in the last position. This is the original probability distribution with one added piece of information, $P(A^c B^c C) = 0$. Call for mincalc. What happens to the probabilities for minterms 0, 1? What can you conclude about mincalc and groups of minterms with total probability zero?

Conditional Probability, Independence, and Conditional Independence

PREVIEW

The probability $P(A)$ of an event A is a measure of the likelihood that the event will occur on any trial. Sometimes partial information determines that an event C has occurred. Given this information, it may be necessary to reassign the likelihood for each event A. This leads to the notion of conditional probability. For a fixed conditioning event C, this assignment to all events constitutes a new probability measure which has all the properties of the original probability measure. In addition, because of the way it is derived from the original, the conditional probability measure has a number of special properties which are important in applications. Although we make limited use of special MATLAB procedures for conditional probabilities, we review some of these properties as the basis for independence and conditional independence.

The notion of stochastic (i.e. probabilistic) independence is based on the idea of lack of conditioning. If knowledge of the occurrence (or nonoccurrence) of an event B does not affect the likelihood of the occurrence of event A, then it seems reasonable to consider the pair $\{A, B\}$ to be independent. This finds expression in the product rule $P(AB) = P(A)P(B)$. The concept extends to arbitrary classes by requiring the product rule to hold for every *finite* subclass of two or more events in the class. It follows that if any event in an independent class is replaced by its complement, the result is still an independent class. This implies that the probabilities of the minterms generated by a finite, independent class are all determined by the probabilities of the basic events in the class.

With the aid of a special sorting procedure, *csort*, the minterm vector procedures, and the MATLAB function *prod*, a variety of problems are solved easily with MATLAB. As an important and illustrative application, we consider the reliability of a system with independent components.

A pattern of *conditional independence* is shown to be useful and is examined briefly. Several simple applications, including one on classifications, demonstrate the usefulness of the concept and the manner in which MATLAB may be employed.

Bernoulli sequences serve to model many repetitive phenomena. These are intimately related to the binomial distribution. A Bernoulli trial generator and functions for calculating binomial probabilities are developed and applied.

1. CONDITIONAL PROBABILITY

DEFINITION AND BASIC PROPERTIES

Original or prior probability utilizes all available information to make probability assignments $P(A)$, $P(B)$, etc., subject to the defining properties (P1), (P2), (P3). The probability $P(A)$ indicates the *likelihood* that event A will occur on any trial.

Frequently, *new information* determines a *conditioning event C*. This may call for reassessing the likelihood of event A. Experience with the classical case suggests the following procedure for reassignment.

Definition   If C is an event having positive probability, the **conditional probability of A, given** C, is

$$P(A \mid C) = \frac{P(AB)}{P(C)}$$

For a fixed conditioning event C, we have a new likelihood assignment to the event A. It is very easy to show that this new function $P(\cdot \mid C)$ satisfies the three defining properties (P1), (P2), and (P3) for probability. Thus, for fixed C, we have a *new probability measure,* with all the properties of an ordinary probability measure.

In addition to its properties as a probability measure, conditional probability has *special properties* which are consequences of the way it is related to the original probability measure $P(\cdot)$. The following are easily derived from the definition of conditional probability and basic properties of the prior probability measure.

(CP1) **Product rule.** If $P(ABCD) > 0$, then $P(ABCD) = P(A)P(B \mid A)P(C \mid AB)P(D \mid ABC)$.

(CP2) **Law of total probability.** Suppose the class $\{A_i: 1 \leq i \leq n\}$ of events is mutually exclusive and every outcome in E is in one of these events. Thus, $E = A_1E \uplus A_2E \uplus \cdots \uplus A_nE$, a disjoint union. Then

$$P(E) = P(E \mid A_1)P(A_1) + P(E \mid A_2)P(A_2) + \cdots + P(E \mid A_n)P(A_n)$$

(CP3) **Bayes' rule.** If E and $\{A_i: 1 \leq i \leq n\}$ are related as in the law of total probability, then

The law of total probability is used to determine $P(E)$.

$$P(A_i \mid E) = \frac{P(A_iE)}{P(E)} = \frac{P(E \mid A_i)P(A_i)}{P(E)} \qquad 1 \leq i \leq n$$

Note that Bayes' rule produces a reversal of "direction" of conditioning. We begin with $P(E \mid A_i)$ and obtain $P(A_i \mid E)$. Such reversals play an important role in many applications. See *PA*, Chapter 3 for examples.

(CP3*) **Ratio form of Bayes' rule.**

$$\frac{P(A \mid C)}{P(B \mid C)} = \frac{P(AC)}{P(BC)} = \frac{P(C \mid A)}{P(C \mid B)} \cdot \frac{P(A)}{P(B)}$$

The left-hand member is called the **posterior odds,** which are the odds *after* knowledge of the occurrence of the conditioning event. The second fraction in the right-hand member is the **prior odds,** which is the odds *before* knowledge of the occurrence of the conditioning event C. The first fraction in the right-hand member is known as the **likelihood ratio.** It is the ratio of the probabilities (or likelihoods) of C for the two different probability measures $P(\cdot \mid A)$ and $P(\cdot \mid B)$.

The following property provides a basis for interpreting conditional probability, and serves to establish a number of important properties for the concept of independence of events.

(CP4) **Some equivalent conditions.** If $0 < P(A) < 1$ and $0 < P(B) < 1$, then

$$P(A \mid B) * P(A) \quad \text{iff } P(B \mid A) * P(B) \quad \text{iff } P(AB) * P(A)P(B) \quad \text{and}$$

$$P(AB) * P(A)P(B) \quad \text{iff } P(A^cB^c) * P(A^c)P(B^c) \quad \text{iff } P(AB^c) \diamond P(A)P(B^c)$$

where $*$ is $<, \leq, =, \geq,$ or $>$ and $\diamond$ is $>, \geq, =, \leq,$ or $<$, respectively.

REPEATED CONDITIONING

Suppose conditioning by the event C has occurred. Additional information is then received that event D has occurred. We have a new conditioning event CD. There are two possibilities:

1. Reassign the conditional probabilities: $P_C(A)$ becomes

$$P_C(A \mid D) = \frac{P_C(AD)}{P_C(D)}.$$

2. Reassign the total probabilities: $P(A)$ becomes

$$P_{CD}(A) = P(A \mid CD) = \frac{P(ACD)}{P(CD)} \, .$$

Basic result: $P_C(A \mid D) = P(A \mid CD) = P_D(A \mid C)$. Thus, repeated conditioning by two events may be done in any order or may be done in one step. This result extends easily to repeated conditioning by any finite number of events. This result is important in many problems involving probable inference.

MATLAB's use in dealing with conditional probability is essentially as an easily used calculator, since it is so easy to enter data and perform the elementary calculations. However, one useful procedure for dealing with Bayes' rule is the following.

—————————————— MATLAB Script ——————————————

```
% file bayes.m
% Version of 7/6/93
disp('Requires input PEA = [P(E|A1) P(E|A2) ... P(E|An)]')
disp(' and PA = [P(A1) P(A2) ... P(An)]')
disp('Determines PAE  = [P(A1|E) P(A2|E) ... P(An|E)]')
disp('        and PAEc = [P(A1|Ec) P(A2|Ec) ... P(An|Ec)]')
PEA  = input('Enter matrix PEA of conditional probabilities  ');
PA   = input('Enter matrix  PA of probabilities  ');
PE   = PEA*PA';
PAE  = (PEA.*PA)/PE;
PAEc = ((1 - PEA).*PA)/(1 - PE);
disp(['P(E) = ',num2str(PE),])
disp(' ')
disp('    P(E|Ai)   P(Ai)     P(Ai|E)    P(Ai|Ec)')
disp([PEA; PA; PAE; PAEc]')
disp('Various quantities are in the matrices named above')
```

———

●———————

EXAMPLE 2.1   A distributor buys "identical" items from four manufacturers and packages them under his own label. An occasional unit fails to meet specifications and must be replaced. A substandard unit is sold. What is the probability it came from any one of the manufacturers? The following data are available: if $E =$ the event a randomly selected unit is substandard and $A_i =$ the event the unit is from the ith manufacturer, then

$$PEA = [P(E \mid A_1) \ P(E \mid A_2) \ P(E \mid A_3) \ P(E \mid A_4)] = [0.05 \ 0.04 \ 0.01 \ 0.07]$$
$$PA = [P(A_1) \ P(A_2) \ P(A_3) \ P(A_4)] = [0.2 \ 0.2 \ 0.5 \ 0.1]$$

We wish to determine $P(A_i \mid E)$ for each i. The MATLAB procedure also determines $P(A_i \mid E^c)$ for each i.

```
>>PA = 0.1*[2 2 5 1];
>>PEA = 0.01*[5 4 1 7];
>>bayes
Requires input PEA = [P(E|A1) P(E|A2) ... P(E|An)]
 and PA = [P(A1) P(A2) ... P(An)]
Determines PAE  = [P(A1|E) P(A2|E) ... P(An|E)]
      and PAEc = [P(A1|Ec) P(A2|Ec) ... P(An|Ec)]
Enter matrix PEA of conditional probabilities P(E|Ai)    PEA
Enter matrix  PA of probabilities P(Ai)    PA
    P(E)     % Probability of getting a defective unit from the distributor
    0.0300
    P(E|Ai)   P(Ai)     P(Ai|E)    P(Ai|Ec)
    0.0500    0.2000    0.3333     0.1959
    0.0400    0.2000    0.2667     0.1979
    0.0100    0.5000    0.1667     0.5103
    0.0700    0.1000    0.2333     0.0959
Various quantities are in the matrices PEA, PA, PAE, PAEc, named above
```

————————————————————————————●

2. INDEPENDENCE OF EVENTS
———————————————————■————

DEFINITION AND BASIC PROPERTIES

In probability theory, we suppose two events form an independent pair iff knowledge of the occurrence of either of the events does not affect the uncertainty about the occurrence of the other. In terms of conditional probability, it seems appropriate to model this lack of conditioning by the requirement

$$P(A \mid B) = P(A) \quad \text{or, equivalently,} \quad P(B \mid A) = P(B)$$

The properties of conditional probability, particularly (CP4), may be used to establish the following:

Sixteen equivalent conditions

$P(A \mid B) = P(A)$	$P(B \mid A) = P(B)$	$P(AB) = P(A)P(B)$
$P(A \mid B^c) = P(A)$	$P(B^c \mid A) = P(B^c)$	$P(AB^c) = P(A)P(B^c)$
$P(A^c \mid B) = P(A^c)$	$P(B \mid A^c) = P(B)$	$P(A^c B) = P(A^c)P(B)$
$P(A^c \mid B^c) = P(A^c)$	$P(B^c \mid A^c) = P(B^c)$	$P(A^c B^c) = P(A^c)P(B^c)$

$$P(A \mid B) = P(A \mid B^c) \quad P(A^c \mid B) = P(A^c \mid B^c) \quad P(B \mid A) = P(B \mid A^c) \quad P(B^c \mid A) = P(B^c \mid A^c)$$

These conditions are equivalent in the sense that if any one holds, then all hold. We may choose any one of these as the defining condition and consider the others as equivalents for the defining condition. Because of its simplicity and symmetry with respect to the two events, we adopt the *product rule* in the upper right-hand corner of the table.

Definition   The pair $\{A, B\}$ of events is said to be (stochastically) **independent** iff the following *product rule* holds:

$$P(AB) = P(A)P(B)$$

Remark: Although the product rule is adopted as the basis for definition, in many applications the assumptions leading to independence may be formulated more naturally in terms of one or more of the equivalent expressions. We are free to do this, for the effect of assuming any one condition is to assume them all.

The product rule is used to extend the concept of independence to an arbitrary *class* of events, as follows.

Definition   A **class** of events is said to be **independent** iff the product rule holds for every finite subclass of two or more events in the class.

Some elementary, but tedious, arguments may be used to establish the following essential fact.

Replacement Rule

If a class is independent, we may replace any of the sets by its complement, by a null event, or by an almost sure event (i.e., an event with probability one), and the resulting class is also independent. Such replacements may be made for any number of the sets in the class.

One immediate and important consequence is the following:

Minterm Probabilities

If $\{A_i: 1 \leq i \leq n\}$ is an independent class and the class $\{P(A_i): 1 \leq i \leq n\}$ of individual probabilities is known, then the probability of every minterm may be calculated.

Again, elementary arguments, utilizing the product rule and minterm expansions, may be used to verify the following.

Boolean Combinations

Let **A** *be an independent class of events. Suppose* $\mathbf{A}_1, \mathbf{A}_2, \cdots, \mathbf{A}_k$ *are subclasses of* **A** *such that no event is included in more than one subclass. If* $F_1, F_2, \cdots, F_k$ *are Boolean combinations of the events in the respective subclasses, then* $\{F_1, F_2, \cdots, F_k\}$ *is an independent class.*

These highly intuitive results give great freedom in dealing with independent classes.

ELEMENTARY MATLAB PROCEDURES

We develop several user defined procedures for dealing with some common problems involving independent events. However, many problems can be dealt with by utilizing directly the appropriate MATLAB functions. We illustrate one such possibility.

EXAMPLE 2.2

Frequently we have an independent class $\{E_1, E_2, \cdots, E_n\}$ and wish to determine probabilities of various "and" combinations (intersections) of the events or their complements. One way of handling it is the following:

Suppose the independent class $\{E_1, E_2, \cdots, E_{10}\}$ has respective probabilities $\{0.13\ 0.37\ 0.12\ 0.56\ 0.33\ 0.71\ 0.22\ 0.43\ 0.57\ 0.31\}$. It is desired to calculate (a) $P(E_1 E_2 E_3^c E_4 E_5^c E_6^c E_7)$ and (b) $P(E_1^c E_2 E_3^c E_4 E_5^c E_6^c E_7 E_8 E_9^c E_{10})$

We may use the MATLAB function **prod** and the scheme for indexing a matrix.

——————————————— MATLAB Script ———————————————

```
>> p = 0.01*[13 37 12 56 33 71 22 43 57 31];
>> q = 1-p;
>> % First case
>> e = [1 2 4 7];           % Uncomplemented positions
>> f = [3 5 6];             % Complemented positions
>> P = prod(p(e))*prod(q(f))  % p(e) probs of uncomplemented factors
P = 0.0010                  % q(f) probs of complemented factors
>> % Case of uncomplemented in even positions; complemented in odd
   % positions
>> e = rem(1:10,2) == 0;    % ones in even positions
>> f = rem(1:10,2) ~= 0;    % ones in odd positions
>> P = prod(p(e))*prod(q(f))
  P = 0.0034
```

A SORTING FUNCTION AND APPLICATIONS

We next introduce a very useful sorting function, which we utilize as a subroutine in a number of functions and procedures.

———————————— MATLAB Script ————————————

```
function  d = csort(T,P)
% T, P are matrices of real values, combined as rows of D
% The pair is sorted on T:
%          * Identical values in T are consolidated
%          * Corresponding values in P are added
D = [T;P];
[Y,I] = sort(T);
X = D(:,I);
m = length(T);
TI = X(1,:);
PI = X(2,:);
j = 1;
t(1) = TI(1);
p(1) = PI(1);
for i = 1:(m - 1)
  if abs(TI(i+1) - TI(i+)) < 1e-6   % Identifies values differing by
                                    % roundoff
     j = j;
     p(j) =  p(j) + PI(i+1);
  else
     j = j+1;
     t(j) = TI(i+1);
     p(j) = PI(i+1);
  end
end
d = [t;p];
```

One use for this procedure is to sort and consolidate the values of T and count the number of occurrences of each of the distinct values. To do this, simply define T, then let $P = \text{ones}(\text{size}(T))$. Then $H = \text{csort}(T, P)$ provides the desired sorting and counting. The procedure has been put in an m-file freq.m as follows:

———————————— MATLAB Script ————————————

```
%  file freq.m
% Version of 11/24/93
% sorts list and counts frequencies
T = input('Enter list to be sorted as row matrix  ');
n = length(T);
```

Continues

```
P = ones(size(T));
H = csort(T,P)';
A = [H H(:,2)/n];
disp(['The number of entries in the list is  ',num2str(n),] )
disp(n)
disp('   Values    Count    Rel Freq')
disp(A)
```

●────────

EXAMPLE 2.3

A sorting example

────────────────────── MATLAB Script ──────────────────────

```
T = [2  0  7  7  9  4  5  8  0  1  5  7  0  4  1  4  7  6  9  8];
>> freq
Enter list to be sorted as row matrix   T
The number of entries in the list is 20
     Values          Count         Rel Freq
          0         3.0000          0.1500
     1.0000         2.0000          0.1000
     2.0000         1.0000          0.0500
     4.0000         3.0000          0.1500
     5.0000         2.0000          0.1000
     6.0000         1.0000          0.0500
     7.0000         4.0000          0.2000
     8.0000         2.0000          0.1000
     9.0000         2.0000          0.1000
```

──●

We now consider several procedures and functions useful in handling independent classes.

THE FUNCTION MINPROB

────────────────────── MATLAB Script ──────────────────────

```
function  y = minprob(p)
% Version of 9/8/93
% Assumes the function mintable
% p is a vector [P(A1) P(A2) ... P(An)]
% y is the row vector of minterm probabilities
n = length(p);
M = mintable(n);
a = p'*ones(1,2^n);          % 2^n columns, each the vector p
m = a.*M + (1 - a).*(1 - M); % Puts probabilities into the minterm
                             % pattern on its side (n by 2^n)
y = prod(m);                 % Product of each column of m
```

EXAMPLE 2.4

—————————————— MATLAB Script ——————————————

```
>> P = minprob(0.1*[4 7 6])
P = 0.0720   0.1080   0.1680   0.2520   0.0480   0.0720   0.1120   0.1680
```

Once we have the matrix *pm* of minterm probabilities, we may calculate the probability of any Boolean combination, as we did in the procedure mincalc in Chapter 1.

EXAMPLE 2.5 The class $\{A, B, C\}$ is independent with corresponding probabilities $\{0.4, 0.3, 0.8\}$. Determine the probabilities of the events $E = A \cup BC^c$ and $F = A(B \cup C^c) \uplus A^c(B^c \cup C)$.

Solution —————————————— MATLAB Script ——————————————

```
>> p = 0.1*[4 3 8];
>> pm = minprob(p);
>> minvec3
>> E = A|(B&Cc);
>> F = (A&(B|Cc))|(Ac&(Bc|C));
>> PE = E*pm'
PE = 0.4360
>> PF = F*pm'
PF = 0.7400
```

Note that this is not necessarily the most efficient way to calculate the probability of one or two Boolean combinations. We can often express the combination in a manner that minimizes computations.

EXAMPLE 2.6 In the example above, $E = A \uplus A^c BC^c$, so that

$$P(E) = P(A) + P(A^c)P(B)P(C^c) = 0.4 + 0.6 \times 0.3 \times 0.2 = 0.436$$

Similarly,

$$P(F) = P(A)[P(B) + P(B^c)P(C^c)] + P(A^c)[P(B^c) + P(B)P(C)]$$
$$= 0.4(0.3 + 0.7 \times 0.2) + 0.6(0.7 + 0.3 \times 0.8) = 0.7400$$

Sometimes, with the aid of the general rules, a larger problem may be decomposed into smaller problems which are easier to handle.

EXAMPLE 2.7

Consider again the independent class $\{E_1, E_2, \cdots, E_{10}\}$ with respective probabilities $\{0.13\ 0.37\ 0.12\ 0.56\ 0.33\ 0.71\ 0.22\ 0.43\ 0.57\ 0.31\}$. We wish to calculate

$$P(F) = P(E_1 \cup E_3(E_4 \cup E_7^c) \cup E_2(E_5^c \cup E_6E_8) \cup E_9E_{10}^c)$$

We could, of course, use minprob to calculate the $2^{10} = 1024$ minterms for all ten of the E_i and determine the minterm vector for F. Note, however, that

$$F = A \cup B \cup C, \quad \text{where } A = E_1 \cup E_3(E_4 \cup E_7^c),$$
$$B = E_2(E_5^c \cup E_6E_8), \quad \text{and} \quad C = E_9E_{10}^c$$

We may calculate directly $P(C) = 0.57 \times 0.69 = 0.3933$. Now A is a Boolean combination of $\{E_1, E_3, E_4, E_7\}$ and B is a combination of $\{E_2, E_5, E_6, E_8\}$. By the rule of Boolean combinations, the class $\{A, B, C\}$ is independent. We use the MATLAB procedures to calculate $P(A)$ and $P(B)$. Then we deal with the independent class $\{A, B, C\}$ to obtain the probability of F.

_____ MATLAB Script _____

```
>> p = 0.01*[13 37 12 56 33 71 22 43 57 31];
>> pa = p([1 3 4 7]);      % Selection of probabilities for A
>> pb = p([2 5 6 8]);      % Selection of probabilities for B
>> pma = minprob(pa);      % Minterms for calculating P(A)
>> pmb = minprob(pb);
>> a = A|(B&(C|Dc));       % A corresponds to E1, B to E3, C to E4, D to E7
>> PA = a*pma'
PA = 0.2243
>> b = A&(Bc|(C&D));       % A corresponds to E2, B to E5, C to E6, D to E8
>> PB = b*pmb'
PB = 0.2852
>> PC = p(9)*(1 - p(10))
PC = 0.3933
>> pm = minprob([PA PB PC]);
>> minvec3                 % The problem becomes a three variable problem
>> F = A|B|C;              % with {A,B,C} an independent class
>> PF = F*pm'
PF = 0.6636
```

_____

This result can be obtained by straightforward calculation of $P(A)$, $P(B)$, and $P(C)$, but the MATLAB procedure is easy to use and less likely to produce errors.

We may have the minterm probabilities for the class $\{A, B, C\}$—say by the use of mincalc—and wish to determine whether or not the class is independent. The following example points the way to a new function.

EXAMPLE 2.8

CHAPTER 2

_____ MATLAB Script _____

```
>> pm = 0.0001*[504 336 756 504 1180 784 1760 1176 ...
              216 144 324 216 500 336 760 504];
>> disp(reshape(pm,4,4))
    0.0504    0.1180    0.0216    0.0500    % Arranged as on minterm map
    0.0336    0.0784    0.0144    0.0336
    0.0756    0.1760    0.0324    0.0760
    0.0504    0.1176    0.0216    0.0504
>> P = mintable(4)*pm';                     % Calculates P(A), P(B), P(C),
                                            % P(D)
>> pt = minprob(P');                        % minprobs for independent case
>> d = abs(pt - pm) > 1e-7;                 % Comparison— roundoff errors
                                            % masked
>> disp(reshape(d,4,4))
    0    1    0    1                         % Minterms where product
                                            % rule fails
    0    0    0    0                         % marked by ones.  Not
                                            % independent
    0    1    0    1
    0    0    0    0
```

We develop a function whose argument is a vector of minterm probabilities. It checks for feasible size, determines the number of variables, and performs a check for independence, as in Example 2.8, above.

_____ MATLAB Script _____

```
function y = imintest(pm)
% Checks minterm probabilities for independence
% Version of 11/24/93
m = length(pm);
n = round(log(m)/log(2));
if m ~= 2^n
  disp('Number of minterm probabilities incorrect')
else
P = mintable(n)*pm';
pt = minprob(P');
a = fix(n/2);
s = abs(pm - pt) > 1e-7;
if sum(s) > 0
  disp('The class is NOT independent')
else
  disp('The class is independent')
end
y = reshape(s,2^a,2^(n-a));
disp(' Minterms with different probabilities')
end
```

This procedure applied to the minterm probabilities in Example 2.8 gives the same result. Consider another example.

● ────────

EXAMPLE 2.9 ─────────── MATLAB Script ───────────────

```
>> pm = 0.01*[15 5 2 18 25 5 18 12];
>> d = imintest(pm)
The class is NOT independent
 Minterms with different probabilities
d =
      1     1     1     0
      1     1     1     0
```

THE PROBABILITY OF *k* OF *n* INDEPENDENT EVENTS

The following programs calculate the probability that k of n independent events will occur, provided the probabilities of the individual events are known. If all these probabilities are the same, then use of the programs for the binomial distribution, introduced in Section 4, may be more efficient. Modifications of the following programs are easily made when the probabilities of the minterms generated by the events are known (whether or not the class is independent). The step pm = minprob(P) is omitted and the matrix pm of the 2^n minterm probabilities is used directly.

────────────────── MATLAB Script ──────────────────

```
function y = ikn(P,k)
% Individual probabilities of k of n successes
% Version of 1/28/93
% Assumes mintable, minprob, csort
n = length(P);
T = sum(mintable(n));   % The number of successes in each minterm
pm = minprob(P);        % The probability of each minterm
d = csort(T,pm);        % Sorts and consolidates success numbers
p= d(2,:);              %   and adds corresponding probabilities
y = p(k+1);
```

A similar procedure calculates the probability of k or more occurrences.

────────────────── MATLAB Script ──────────────────

```
function y = ckn(P,k)
% Probabilities of k or more of n
```

Continues

```
% Version of 11/27/93
% Assumes mintable, minprob, csort
n = length(P);
m = length(k);
T = sum(mintable(n));   % The number of successes in each minterm
pm = minprob(P);        % The probability of each minterm
d = csort(T,pm);        % Sorts and consolidates success numbers
p= d(2,:);              %    and adds corresponding probabilities
for i = 1:m             % Sums probabilities for each k value
  y(i) = sum(p(k(i)+1:n+1));
end
```

EXAMPLE 2.10

A Numerical
Example

———————— MATLAB Script ————————

```
>>p = 0.01*[13 37 12 56 33 71 22 43 57 31];
>>k = [2 5 7];
>>P = ckn(p,k)
P =    0.9516    0.2921    0.0266
>>PI = ikn(p,k)
PI =   0.1401    0.1845    0.0225
```

RELIABILITY OF A SYSTEM OF INDEPENDENT COMPONENTS

Suppose a system has n components which fail independently. Let E_i be the event the ith component survives the designated time period. Then $R_i = P(E_i)$ is defined to be the *reliability* of that component. The reliability R of the complete system is a function of the components' reliabilities. There are three basic configurations. General systems may be decomposed into subsystems of these types. The subsystems become components in the larger configuration. The three fundamental configurations are:

1. **Series.** The system operates iff *all* n components operate:

$$R = \prod_{i=1}^{n} R_i.$$

2. **Parallel.** The system operates if *any* one or more components operate:

$$R = 1 - \prod_{i=1}^{n} (1 - R_i).$$

3. **k of n.** The system operates iff k or more components operate. R is the sum of the probabilities of those minterms generated by $\{E_1, E_2, \cdots, E_n\}$ with k or more successes.

MATLAB Solution.   Put the component reliabilities in matrix $RC = [R1 \; R2 \; \cdots \; Rn]$.

1. Series Configuration

───────────────── MATLAB Script ─────────────────

```
>> R = prod(RC)      % prod is a MATLAB function
```

2. Parallel Configuration

───────────────── MATLAB Script ─────────────────

```
>> R = parallel(RC)  % parallel is a user defined function
                     % y = 1 - prod(1 - RC)   (in file parallel.m)
```

3. k of n Configuration

───────────────── MATLAB Script ─────────────────

```
>> R = ckn(RC,k)     % ckn is a user defined function
                     % (in file ckn.m). If all
                     % component probabilities are the same,
                     % use cbinom(n,p,k).
```

EXAMPLE 2.11   There are eight components, numbered 1 through 8. Component 1 is in series with a parallel combination of components 2 and 3, followed by a 3 of 5 combination of components 4 through 8 (see Figure 2.1). Probabilities of the components in order are

$$0.95 \quad 0.90 \quad 0.92 \quad 0.80 \quad 0.83 \quad 0.91 \quad 0.85 \quad 0.85$$

The second and third probabilities are for the parallel pair, and the last five probabilities are for the 3 of 5 combination.

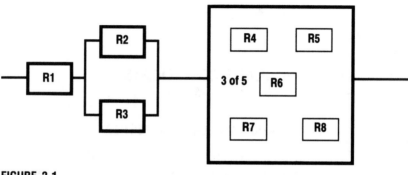

FIGURE 2.1

```
>> RC = 0.01*[95 90 92 80 83 91 85 85];          % Component
                                                 % reliabilities 1–8
>> Ra = RC(1)*parallel(RC(2:3))*ckn(RC(4:8),3)   % Solution
Ra = 0.9172
```

EXAMPLE 2.12 Consider a second arrangement of the eight components in the previous system. Components 1 and 2 are in series with a parallel combination of component 3 with a 3 of 5 combination of components 5 through 8 (see Figure 2.2).

_____ MATLAB Script _____

```
>> RC = 0.01*[95 90 92 80 83 91 85 85];                    % Component
                                                           % reliabilities 1–8
>> Rb = prod(RC(1:2))*parallel([RC(3),ckn(RC(4:8),3)])     % Solution
Rb = 0.8532
```

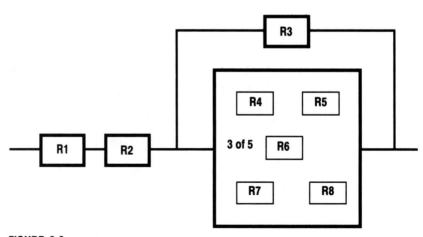

FIGURE 2.2

3. CONDITIONAL INDEPENDENCE OF EVENTS

DEFINITION AND BASIC PROPERTIES

There is a wide variety of situations in which independence of a pair of events is "conditioned" by an event which reflects a common chance factor.

EXAMPLE 2.13
Independent
Medical Tests

A doctor orders "independent" laboratory tests on a patient for a suspected pathology. Suppose D = the event the patient has the suspected condition. Let E_1 = the event the first test is positive (i.e., indicates the disease) and E_2 = the event the second test is positive. Is it reasonable to suppose the pair $\{E_1, E_2\}$ is independent? If so, then one or more of the tests must be useless. Both should be tied to the condition of the patient with respect to the pathological condition. Thus, we should *not* expect $P(E_1 \mid E_2) = P(E_1 \mid E_2^c)$. In fact, we should expect $P(E_1 \mid E_2) > P(E_1 \mid E_2^c)$. In what sense are the tests independent? Given the condition of the patient, neither test is affected by the result of the other. Therefore it would seem reasonable to suppose that $P(E_1 \mid DE_2) = P(E_1 \mid DE_2^c)$. That is, the outcome of Test 1 is unaffected by the outcome of Test 2, given that the patient has the disease. Similarly, we should expect $P(E_1 \mid D^c E_2) = P(E_1 \mid D^c E_2^c)$.

EXAMPLE 2.14
Polls and Public
Opinion

Two polls are taken by professional organizations to determine public views on a candidate. The organizations operate independently, neither knowing the results of the other's investigation. Let H = the event the candidate is favored, E_1 = the event the first poll indicates the candidate is favored, and E_2 = the event the second poll indicates the candidate is the person of choice. Then, again it seems reasonable to suppose $P(E_1 \mid HE_2) = P(E_1 \mid HE_2^c)$ and $P(E_1 \mid H^c E_2) = P(E_1 \mid H^c E_2^c)$.

EXAMPLE 2.15
Contractors and
Weather

Two contractors are working on different jobs in the same city. Let E_1 = the event the first contractor completes his job on time and E_2 = the event the second contractor meets his target date. The contractors operate independently, yet the pair $\{E_1, E_2\}$ may not be independent. The jobs are outside and are thus affected by the weather. Let G = the event the weather is good enough that work is not delayed. Then $P(E_1 \mid GE_2) = P(E_1 \mid GE_2^c)$ and $P(E_1 \mid G^c E_2) = P(E_1 \mid G^c E_2^c)$.

The same pattern of conditioning holds in all three examples considered. It seems to be symmetric with respect to the common conditioning event (D, H, or E). Next, consider a case in which this symmetry does not hold.

EXAMPLE 2.16
Contractors and
Scarce Material

Consider the contractors of the previous example. Suppose the weather causes no significant delays, but both jobs depend upon a certain material. If H = the event the material is in good supply, then we should assume that $P(E_1 \mid HE_2) = P(E_1 \mid HE_2^c)$. However, if the material is scarce, then we should expect $P(E_1 \mid H^c E_2) < P(E_1 \mid H^c E_2^c)$, for if the second contractor completes on time and material is scarce (event $H^c E_2$ occurs), then it is likely that he has obtained the scarce material to the detriment of the first contractor.

As we show below, the conditions above amount to assuming independence with respect to a conditional probability measure. It is natural to refer to such independence as "conditional independence." We formalize this concept and develop some general patterns which facilitate modeling and analysis in the many practical situations for which it is appropriate. We begin by looking at the formal pattern representing independence with respect to a conditional probability measure $P(\cdot \mid C) = P_C(\cdot)$. In the hybrid notation we use for repeated conditioning, we write

$$P_C(A \mid B) = P_C(A) \quad \text{or} \quad P_C(AB) = P_C(A)P_C(B)$$

This translates into

$$P(A \mid BC) = P(A \mid C) \quad \text{or} \quad P(AB \mid C) = P(A \mid C)P(B \mid C)$$

If it is known that C has occurred, then additional knowledge of the occurrence of B does not change the likelihood of A.

If we write the sixteen equivalent conditions for independence in terms of the conditional probability measure $P_C(\cdot)$ and then translate as above, we have the following equivalent conditions.

Sixteen equivalent conditions

$P(A \mid BC) = P(A \mid C)$	$P(B \mid AC) = P(B \mid C)$	$P(AB \mid C) = P(A \mid C)P(B \mid C)$
$P(A \mid B^c C) = P(A \mid C)$	$P(B^c \mid AC) = P(B^c \mid C)$	$P(AB^c \mid C) = P(A \mid C)P(B^c \mid C)$
$P(A^c \mid BC) = P(A^c \mid C)$	$P(B \mid A^c C) = P(B \mid C)$	$P(A^c B \mid C) = P(A^c \mid C)P(B \mid C)$
$P(A^c \mid B^c C) = P(A^c \mid C)$	$P(B^c \mid A^c C) = P(B^c \mid C)$	$P(A^c B^c \mid C) = P(A^c \mid C)P(B^c \mid C)$

$$P(A \mid BC) = P(A \mid B^c C) \quad P(A^c \mid BC) = P(A^c \mid B^c C) \quad P(B \mid AC) = P(B \mid A^c C) \quad P(B^c \mid AC) = P(B^c \mid A^c C)$$

The patterns of conditioning in the examples of Section 5.1 of *PA* belong to this set. In a given problem, one or the other of these conditions may seem to be a reasonable assumption. As soon as *one* of these patterns is recognized, then *all* are equally valid assumptions. Because of its simplicity and symmetry, we take as the defining condition the *product rule* $P(AB \mid C) = P(A \mid C)P(B \mid C)$.

Definition   A pair of events $\{A, B\}$ is said to be **conditionally independent, given** C, designated $\{A, B\}$ ci $\mid C$, iff the following product rule holds: $P(AB \mid C) = P(A \mid C)P(B \mid C)$.

The equivalence of the four entries in the right-hand column of the upper part of the table establishes

The Replacement Rule

If any of the pairs $\{A, B\}$, $\{A, B^c\}$, $\{A^c, B\}$, or $\{A^c, B^c\}$ is conditionally independent, given C, then so are the others.

Examples show that we may have $\{A, B\}$ ci $|C$ and $\{A, B\}$ ci $|C^c$ and yet *not* have independence. On the other hand, we may have conditional independence, given C, but not conditional independence, given C^c. As shown in Example 2.16, the contractors and scarce material, such situations arise when some chance factor has an asymmetrical effect on the two events in question.

An examination of the relations involved shows that only in very special cases is it true that a pair $\{A, B\}$ is conditionally independent with respect to both C and C^c and also is independent.

Since the concept is that of independence with respect to a conditional probability measure, which is a probability measure in its own right, extensions to larger classes are straightforward.

Definition

A class $\{E_i : 1 \le i \le n\}$ is said to be conditionally independent, given H, designated $\{E_i : 1 \le i \le n\}$ ci $|H$, iff the following *product rule* holds for any finite subclass $\{E_i : i \in J\}$ of two or more events.

$$P\left(\bigcap_J^n E_i \mid H\right) = \prod_J^n P(E_i \mid H)$$

As in the case of independence with respect to the total probability, we have a *replacement rule* and resulting patterns for minterm probabilities and for conditional independence of Boolean combinations. Thus, we handle conditional probabilities of conditionally independent events as in the case of ordinary independence. The rule on minterms shows the computational advantage of conditional independence. It is only necessary to know n conditional probabilities to determine the conditional probability of any Boolean combination. Without this condition, $2^n - 1$ pieces of information are required to determine the conditional probability of every Boolean combination.

We do not give a full treatment of this topic, since for many patterns we do not have special MATLAB procedures or functions. For a fuller discussion and consideration of a variety of significant examples, see *PA*, Chapter 5.

USE OF INDEPENDENCE TECHNIQUES

EXAMPLE 2.17
An Investment Problem

Jane is contemplating an investment which she thinks has a probability of 0.7 of being successful. She checks on five "independent" indicators. If the investment is sound, the probabilities are 0.8, 0.75, 0.6, 0.9, and 0.8 that the indicators will be positive; if the investment is not sound, the respective probabilities are 0.75, 0.85, 0.7, 0.9, and 0.7 that the indicators will be negative. Given the quality of the investment, the indicators are independent of one another in the sense that no indicator is affected by the others. Of course, they are not independent, for they are all related to the soundness of the investment. We may reasonably assume conditional independence of the indicators, given the investment is sound and also given the investment is not sound. If Jane goes with the majority of indications, what is the probability she will make the right decision?

Solution   If the investment is sound, Jane makes the right choice if three or more of the five indicators are positive. If the investment is unsound, she makes the right choice if three or more of the five indicators are negative. Let H be the event the investment is sound, F be the event three or more indicators are positive, $G = F^c$ is the event three or more are negative, and $S =$ the event of the correct decision. Then

$$P(S) = P(FH) + P(GH^c) = P(F \mid H)P(H) + P(G \mid H^c)P(H^c)$$

Let E_i be the event the ith indicator is positive. Then $P(F \mid H) =$ the sum of probabilities of the form $P(M_k \mid H)$, where M_k are minterms generated by the class $\{E_i: 1 \le i \le 5\}$. Because of the assumed conditional independence,

$$P(E_1 E_2^c E_3^c E_4 E_5 \mid H) = P(E_1 \mid H)P(E_2^c \mid H)P(E_3^c \mid H)P(E_4 \mid H)P(E_5 \mid H)$$

with similar expressions for each $P(M_k \mid H)$ and $P(M_k \mid H^c)$. This means that if we want the probability of three or more successes, given H, we can use ckn with the matrix of conditional probabilities. A MATLAB solution of the investment problem is as follows.

———————————————— MATLAB Script ————————————————

```
>> P1 = 0.01*[80 75 60 90 80];
>> P2 = 0.01*[75 85 70 90 70];
>> PH = 0.7;
>> PS = ckn(P1,3)*PH + ckn(P2,3)*(1 - PH)
PS =    0.9255
```

The problems in the following section are illustrative of a considerable class of inference problems. Although the calculations are straightforward, they involve a data selection procedure which is tedious and error prone.

CLASSIFICATION ON THE BASIS OF A PROFILE

A population consists of members of two subgroups. It is desired to formulate a battery of questions to aid in identifying the subclass membership of randomly selected individuals in the population. The questions are designed so that for each individual the answers are independent, in the sense that the answers to any subset of these questions is not affected by and does not affect the answers to any other subset of the questions. Consider the following example.

EXAMPLE 2.18
A Classification Problem

A sample of 125 subjects is taken from a population which has two subgroups. The subgroup membership of each subject in the sample is known. Each one is asked a battery of ten questions designed to be independent, in the sense that the answer to any one is not affected by the answer to any other. The subjects answer independently. Data on the results are summarized in the following table.

Q	GROUP 1 (69 members)			GROUP 2 (56 members)		
	Yes	No	Unc.	Yes	No	Unc.
1	42	22	5	20	31	5
2	34	27	8	16	37	3
3	15	45	9	33	19	4
4	19	44	6	31	18	7
5	22	43	4	23	28	5
6	41	13	15	14	37	5
7	9	52	8	31	17	8
8	40	26	3	13	38	5
9	48	12	9	27	24	5
10	20	37	12	35	16	5

Assume the data are representative of the entire population consisting of these two groups. Then they may be used to calculate probabilities and conditional probabilities for the whole population.

Several persons are interviewed. The result of each interview is a "profile" of answers to the questions. The goal is to classify the person in one of the subgroups on the basis of the profile of answers. The following profiles were taken.

- Y, N, Y, N, Y, U, N, U, Y, U.
- N, N, U, N, Y, Y, U, N, N, Y.
- Y, Y, N, Y, U, U, N, N, Y, Y.

Classify each individual in one of the subgroups.

Solution

Let G_1 = the event the person selected is from Group 1, and $G_2 = G_1^c$ = the event the person selected is from Group 2. Let

A_i = the event the answer to the ith question is "Yes"

B_i = the event the answer to the ith question is "No"

C_i = the event the answer to the ith question is "Uncertain"

The data are taken to mean $P(A_1 \mid G_1) = 42/69$, $P(B_3 \mid G_2) = 19/56$, etc. The profile

$$Y, N, Y, N, Y, U, N, U, Y.$$

U corresponds to the event

$$E = A_1 B_2 A_3 B_4 A_5 C_6 B_7 C_8 A_9 C_{10}$$

We utilize the ratio form of Bayes' rule to calculate the posterior odds

$$\frac{P(G_1 \mid E)}{P(G_2 \mid E)} = \frac{P(E \mid G_1)}{P(E \mid G_2)} \cdot \frac{P(G_1)}{P(G_2)}$$

If the ratio is greater than one, then classify in Group 1; otherwise, classify in Group 2 (we assume that a ratio exactly equal to one is so unlikely that we can neglect it). Because of conditional independence, we are able to determine the conditional probabilities

$$P(E \mid G_1) = \frac{42 \times 27 \times 15 \times 44 \times 22 \times 15 \times 52 \times 3 \times 48 \times 12}{69^{10}} \quad \text{and}$$

$$P(E \mid G_2) = \frac{29 \times 37 \times 33 \times 18 \times 23 \times 5 \times 17 \times 5 \times 24 \times 5}{56^{10}}$$

The odds $P(G_1)/P(G_2) = 69/56$. We find the posterior odds to be

$$\frac{P(G_1 \mid E)}{P(G_2 \mid E)} = \frac{42 \times 27 \times 15 \times 44 \times 22 \times 15 \times 52 \times 3 \times 48 \times 12}{29 \times 37 \times 33 \times 18 \times 23 \times 5 \times 17 \times 5 \times 24 \times 5}$$

$$\cdot \frac{56^9}{69^9} = 5.85$$

The factor $56^9/69^9$ comes from multiplying $56^{10}/69^{10}$ by the odds $P(G_1)/P(G_2) = 69/56$. Since the resulting posterior odds favoring Group 1 is greater than one, we classify the respondent in Group 1.

Answers to the questions would normally be designated by symbols such as Y for yes, N for no, and U for uncertain. In order for the MATLAB procedure to work, these answers must be represented by numbers indicating the appropriate column in matrices A and B. Thus, in the example under consideration, each Y must be translated into a 1, each N into a 2, and each U into a 3. The task is not particularly difficult, but it is much easier to have MATLAB do the job.

The following two-stage procedure for solving the problem works well. The first procedure sets up the frequency information for calculating posterior odds.

──────────────── MATLAB Script ────────────────

```
% file oddsdf.m
% Sets up frequencies for calculating posterior odds
% Veersion of 12/4/93
A = input('Enter matrix A of frequencies for calibration Group 1  ');
B = input('Enter matrix B of frequencies for calibration Group 2  ');
n = length(A(:,1));       % Number of questions (rows of A)
m = length(A(1,:));       % Number of answers to each question
p1 = sum(A(1,:));         % Number in calibration Group 1
p2 = sum(B(1,:));         % Number in calibration Group 2
A = A/p1;
B = B/p2;
disp(' ')                 % Blank line in presentation
disp(['Number of questions = ',num2str(n),])  % Size of profile
disp(' Answers per question = ',num2str(m),]) % Usually 3: yes, no, uncertain
disp(' Enter code for answers and call for procedure "odds"  ')
disp(' ')
```

The next stage calculates the odds for a given profile. The advantage of splitting the solution to the problem into two procedures is that we can set up the data once, then call repeatedly for the calculations for different profiles.

———————————— MATLAB Script ————————————

```
% file odds.m
% Calculates posterior odds for profile E
% Version of 12/4/93
E = input('Enter profile matrix E  ');
C =  diag(A(:,E))';        % a = A(:,E) is an n by n
matrix whose ith column
D =  diag(B(:,E))';        % is the E(i)th column of
A.  The elements on the
                           % diagonal are A(i, E(i)), 1 <= i <= n
                           % Similarly for B(:,E)
R = prod(C./D)*(p1/p2);    % Calculates posterior odds for profile
disp(' ')
disp(['Odds favoring Group 1:   ',num2str(R),])
if R > 1
  disp('Classify in Group 1')
else
  disp('Classify in Group 2')
end
```

We enter the data from an m-file

———————————— MATLAB Script ————————————

```
>> type spec1_2.m  % Data in file spec1_2.m
A = [42 22 5; 34 27 8; 15 45 9; 19 44 6; 22 43 4;
     41 13 15; 9 52 8; 40 26 3; 48 12 9; 20 37 12];
B = [20 31 5; 16 37 3; 33 19 4; 31 18 7; 23 28 5;
     14 37 5; 31 17 8; 13 38 5; 27 24 5; 35 16 5];
>> spec1_2          % Call for data
>> oddsdf           % Call for setup procedure
Enter matrix A of frequencies for calibration Group 1  A
Enter matrix B of frequencies for calibration Group 2  B
 Number of questions = 10
 Answers per question = 3
 Enter code for answers and call for procedure "odds"
>> Y = 1;           % Setup for MATLAB to code profiles
>> N = 2;
>> U = 3;
>> odds             % Call for analyzing the first profile
```

Continues

```
Enter profile matrix E  [Y N Y N Y U N U Y U]
 Odds favoring Group 1:   5.8452
 Classify in Group 1
>> odds             % Call for analyzing the second profile
Enter profile matrix E  [N N U N Y Y U N N Y]
 Odds favoring Group 1:   0.2383
 Classify in Group 2
>> odds             % Call for analyzing the third profile
Enter profile matrix E  [Y Y N Y U U N N Y Y]
 Odds favoring Group 1:   5.0498
 Classify in Group 1
```

The principal feature of the procedure is the scheme for selecting the numbers from the A and B matrices. If $E = [Y\ Y\ N\ Y\ U\ U\ U\ N\ N\ Y\ Y]$, then $A(:, E)$ is a matrix with columns corresponding to elements of E. Thus,

--------------------------------- MATLAB Script ---------------------------------

```
>> e = A(:,E)
e =
    42    42    22    42     5     5    22    22    42    42
    34    34    27    34     8     8    27    27    34    34
    15    15    45    15     9     9    45    45    15    15
    19    19    44    19     6     6    44    44    19    19
    22    22    43    22     4     4    43    43    22    22
    41    41    13    41    15    15    13    13    41    41
     9     9    52     9     8     8    52    52     9     9
    40    40    26    40     3     3    26    26    40    40
    48    48    12    48     9     9    12    12    48    48
    20    20    37    20    12    12    37    37    20    20
```

The ith entry in the ith column is the count corresponding to the answer to the ith question. For example, the answer to the third question is N (no), and the corresponding count is the third entry in the N (second) column of A. The element on the diagonal in the third column of $A(:, E)$ is the third element in that column, and hence the desired third entry of the N column. By picking out the elements on the diagonal by the command diag(A(:, E)), we have the desired set of counts corresponding to the profile. The same is true for diag(B(:, E)).

Sometimes the data are given in terms of conditional probabilities and probabilities. A slight modification of the procedure handles this case. For purposes of comparison, we convert the problem above to this form by converting the counts in matrices A and B to conditional probabilities. We do this by dividing by the total count in each group (69 and 56 in this case). Also, $P(G_1) = 69/125 = 0.552$ and $P(G_2) = 56/125 = 0.448$.

	GROUP 1 $P(G_1) = 0.552$			GROUP 2 $P(G_2) = 0.448$		
Q	Yes	No	Unc.	Yes	No	Unc.
1	0.6087	0.3188	0.0725	0.3571	0.5536	0.0893
2	0.4928	0.3913	0.1159	0.2857	0.6607	0.0536
3	0.2174	0.6522	0.1304	0.5893	0.3393	0.0714
4	0.2754	0.6377	0.0870	0.5536	0.3214	0.1250
5	0.3188	0.6232	0.0580	0.4107	0.5000	0.0893
6	0.5942	0.1884	0.2174	0.2500	0.6607	0.0893
7	0.1304	0.7536	0.1159	0.5536	0.3036	0.1429
8	0.5797	0.3768	0.0435	0.2321	0.6786	0.0893
9	0.6957	0.1739	0.1304	0.4821	0.4286	0.0893
10	0.2899	0.5362	0.1739	0.6250	0.2857	0.0893

The modified MATLAB setup procedure is

—————————————— MATLAB Script ——————————————

```
% file odds dp.m
% Sets up conditional probabilities for odds calculations
% Version of 12/4/93
A = input('Enter conditional probabilities for Group 1  ');
B = input('Enter conditional probabilities for Group 2  ');
p1 = input('Probability p1 individual is from Group 1  ');
n = length(A(:,1));
m = length(A(1,:));
p2 = 1 - p1;
disp(' ')                    % Blank line in presentation
disp(['Number of questions = ',num2str(n),])   % Size of profile
disp(' Answers per question = ',num2str(m),]) % Usually 3: yes, no, uncertain
disp(' Enter code for answers and call for procedure "odds"  ')
disp(' ')
```

We use this procedure and the procedure odds on the converted data above.

—————————————— MATLAB Script ——————————————

```
>> spec1_2p        % call for converted data
>> oddsdp
Enter conditional probabilities for Group 1  Ap
Enter conditional probabilities for Group 2  Bp
Probability p1 individual is from Group 1  0.552
 Number of questions = 10
 Answers per question = 3
 Enter code for answers and call for procedure "odds"
>> Y = 1;
```

Continues

```
>>N = 2;
>>U = 3;
>>odds
Enter profile matrix E  [Y N Y N Y U N U Y U]
Odds favoring Group 1:   5.8464
Classify in Group 1
```

The slight discrepency in the odds favoring Group 1 (5.8464 compared with 5.8452) can be attributed to rounding of the conditional probabilities to four places.

4. BERNOULLI TRIALS AND THE BINOMIAL DISTRIBUTION

THE CONCEPT AND A BERNOULLI TRIAL GENERATOR

Many compound trials may be described as a sequence of *success-failure* trials. On each component trial in the sequence, the outcome is one of two kinds. One we designate a *success* and the other a *failure*. Examples abound: heads or tails in a sequence of coin flips, favor or disapprove of a proposition in a survey sample, and meet or fail to meet specifications in a sequence of quality control checks. To represent the situation, we let E_i be the event of a success on the ith (component) trial in the sequence. We say "component" trial, since the complete trial consists of the whole sequence of component trials. The event of a failure on the ith component trial is E_i^c.

In many cases, we model the sequence as a *Bernoulli sequence,* in which the results on the successive component trials are independent and have the same probabilities. Thus, formally, a sequence of success-failure trials is Bernoulli iff

1. The class $\{E_i: 1 \leq i\}$ is independent.
2. The probability $P(E_i) = p$, invariant with i.

It is frequently desirable to simulate Bernoulli trials. By flipping coins, rolling a die with various numbers of sides (as used in certain games), or using spinners, it is relatively easy to carry this out physically. However, if the number of trials is large—say several hundred—the process may be time consuming. Also, there are limitations on the values of p, the probability of success. The following procedure provides a convenient way to generate such sequences using the random number generator in MATLAB. The procedure is divided into two parts. The first part sets up the parameters. The second part allows easily repeated calls for a sequence.

_____ MATLAB Script _____

```
% file btdata.m
% Bernoulli trials data
n = input('Enter n, the number of trials  ');
p = input('Enter p, the probability of success on each trial  ');
disp(' ')
disp(' Call for bt')
disp(' ')
```

_____ MATLAB Script _____

```
% bt.m
% Bernoulli sequence for btdata
% version of 5/11/94
B = rand(n,1) <= p;        % ones for random numbers <= p
F = sum(B)/n;              % relative frequency of ones
N = [1:n]';                % display details
disp(['n = ',num2str(n),'   p = ',num2str(p),])
disp(['Frequency = ',num2str(F),])
SEQ = [N B];
disp('To view the sequence, call for SEQ')
disp(' ')
```

In the following example, we keep the number of trials small to save space in the printout. Values of *n* of several thousand are handled readily.

●———————

EXAMPLE 2.19

_____ MATLAB Script _____

```
>> btdata
Enter n, the number of trials  20
Enter p, the probability of success on each trial  0.39
Call for bt
>> bt                    % First sequence
n = 20    p = 0.39
Frequency = 0.3
To view the sequence, call for SEQ
>> bt                    % Second sequence. The random number
n = 20    p = 0.39       % generator produces a new sequence.
Frequency = 0.4
To view the sequence, call for SEQ
>> disp(SEQ)             % Call for display of second sequence
1      1
2      0
3      0
4      1
5      0
```

Continues

6	0
7	0
8	1
9	1
10	1
11	1
12	0
13	0
14	0
15	1
16	0
17	0
18	0
19	1
20	0

To illustrate the law of large numbers, n of 10,000 is quite feasible. Three sequences of $n = 10000$, with $p = 0.39$, gave relative frequencies of 0.3876, 0.3945, and 0.3901. As expected, these cluster around 0.39. See Exploration problem 2.5 for a suggested graphic procedure for examining the relative frequency as n increases.

THE BINOMIAL DISTRIBUTION

A basic problem in Bernoulli sequences is to determine the probability of k successes in n component trials. We let $S_n =$ the number of successes in n trials. This is a special case of a simple random variable, which we study in more detail in a subsequent section.

Let us characterize the event $\{S_n = k\}$, $0 \le k \le n$. The event of exactly k successes is the event of one of the minterms generated by $\{E_i: 1 \le i\}$ in which there are k successes (represented by k uncomplemented E_i) and $n - k$ failures (represented by $n - k$ complemented E_i^c). Simple combinatorics show there are $C(n, k)$ ways to choose the k places to be uncomplemented. Hence, among the 2^n minterms, there are $C(n, k) = \frac{n!}{k!(n-k)!}$ which have k factors uncomplemented. Each such minterm has a probability of $p^k(1 - p)^{n-k}$. Since the minterms are mutually exclusive, their probabilities add. We conclude that

$$P(S_n = k) = C(n, k)p^k(1 - p)^{n-k} = C(n, k)p^k q^{n-k} \quad \text{for } 0 \le k \le n$$

These probabilities and the corresponding values form the *distribution* for S_n. This distribution is known as the **binomial distribution,** with parameters (n, p). We shorten this to binomial (n, p), and often write $S_n \sim$ binomial (n, p). A related set of probabilities is $P(S_n \ge k)$, $0 \le k \le n$. Because Bernoulli sequences are used in so many practical situations as models for success-failure trials, the probabilities $P(S_n = k)$ and $P(S_n \ge k)$ have been calculated and tabulated for a variety of combinations of the parameters (n, p). Such tables are found in most mathematical handbooks. Tables of $P(S_n = k)$ are usually given a title such as *binomial distribution, individual terms*. Tables of $P(S_n \geq k)$ have a designation such as *binomial distribution, cumulative terms*. Note, however, some tables for comulative terms give $P(S_n \leq k)$. Care should be taken to note which convention is used. Although tables are convenient for calculation, they put serious limitations on the available parameter values, and when the values are found in a table, they must still be entered into the problem formulation.

We have convenient MATLAB user defined functions for these distributions. When MATLAB is available, it is much easier to generate the needed probabilities than to look them up in a table. In fact, for many parameter values which appear in practice, no tables are available. We note the MATLAB functions and describe briefly their use, but leave more detailed description to Chapter 3.

function y = ibinom(n, p, k) calculates individual binomial probabilities. The parameter n is a positive integer; the parameter p is a probability. Parameter k is a row vector of integers between 0 and n. The result y is a row vector of probabilities $P(X = k)$.

function y = cbinom(n, p, k) calculates cumulative terms $P(X \geq k)$. The parameter n is a positive integer; the parameter p is a probability. Parameter k is a row vector of integers between 0 and n. The result y is a row vector of probabilities $P(X \geq k)$.

● ───────────

EXAMPLE 2.20
Binomial
Probabilities

If $S \sim$ binomial $(10, 0.39)$, determine $P(S = k)$ and $P(S \geq k)$ for $k = 3, 5, 6, 8$.

─────────────── MATLAB Script ───────────────

```
>>p = 0.39;
>>k = [3 5 6 8];
>>Pi = ibinom(10,p,k)  % individual probabilities
Pi = 0.2237   0.1920  0.1023    0.0090
>>Pc = cbinom(10,p,k)  % cumulative probabilities
Pc = 0.8160   0.3420  0.1500    0.0103
```

If a table with a specific range of values is desired, it is easy to use the functions ibinomial and cbinomial to generate the table. The following procedure produces such a table to specifications.

─────────────── MATLAB Script ───────────────

```
% file binomial.m
% Calculates a table of binomial probabilities
% for specified n, p, and row vector k
n = input('Enter n, the number of trials  ');
p = input('Enter p, the probability of success  ');
```

Continues

───

```
k = input('Enter row vector k of success numbers   ');
y = ibinom(n,p,k);                    % calculates individual terms
z = cbinom(n,p,k);                    % calculates cumulative terms
N = ['     n          p'];              % display details
H = ['     k        P(X=k)      P(X>=k)'];
D = [k; y; z]';
disp(' ')
disp(N)
disp([n p])
disp(H)
disp(D)
```

EXAMPLE 2.21
Binomial Tables

————————————————— MATLAB Script ——————————————————

```
>> binomial                              % call for procedure
Enter n, the number of trials   13
Enter p, the probability of success   0.413
Enter row vector k of success numbers   0:13
     n          p
    13.0000   0.4130
     k        P(X=k)      P(X>=k)
     0        0.0010      1.0000
     1.0000   0.0090      0.9990
     2.0000   0.0379      0.9900
     3.0000   0.0979      0.9521
     4.0000   0.1721      0.8542
     5.0000   0.2180      0.6821
     6.0000   0.2045      0.4641
     7.0000   0.1439      0.2596
     8.0000   0.0759      0.1158
     9.0000   0.0297      0.0398
    10.0000   0.0084      0.0102
    11.0000   0.0016      0.0018
    12.0000   0.0002      0.0002
    13.0000   0.0000      0.0000
```

COMPOUND BERNOULLI TRIALS

Often it is desirable to compare the results of two sequences of Bernoulli trials carried out independently. The following example illustrates an approach which demonstrates the utility of the ibinomial and cbinomial functions.

EXAMPLE 2.22
*A Compound
Bernoulli Trial*

Bill and Mary each take ten "free throws" with a basketball. We assume the two sequences of trials are independent of each other, and each is a Bernoulli sequence.

Mary: Has probability 0.80 of success on each trial.

Bill: Has probability 0.85 of success on each trial.

What is the probability Mary makes more free throws than Bill?

Solution

We have two Bernoulli sequences operating independently.

Mary: $n = 10$, $p = 0.80$

Bill: $n = 10$, $p = 0.85$

Let

M be the event Mary wins

M_k be the event Mary makes k or more free throws.

B_j be the event Bill makes exactly j free throws

Then Mary wins if Bill makes none and Mary makes one or more, or Mary wins if Bill makes one and Mary makes two or more, etc. Thus,

$$M = B_0 M_1 \uplus B_1 M_2 \uplus \cdots \uplus B_9 M_{10} \text{ (mutually exclusive)}$$

and

$$P(M) = P(B_0)P(M_1) + P(B_1)P(M_2) + \cdots + P(B_9)P(M_{10})$$

We use MATLAB to calculate the cumulative probabilities for Mary and the individual probabilities for Bill.

_____ MATLAB Script _____

```
>> pm = cbinom(10,0.8,1:10);     % cumulative probabilities for Mary
>> pb = ibinom(10,0.85,0:9);     % individual probabilities for Bill
>> D = [pm; pb]'                 % display: pm in the first column
   D =                          %          pb in the second column
      1.0000    0.0000
      1.0000    0.0000
      0.9999    0.0000
      0.9991    0.0001
      0.9936    0.0012
      0.9672    0.0085
      0.8791    0.0401
      0.6778    0.1298
      0.3758    0.2759
      0.1074    0.3474
```

To find the probability $P(M)$ that Mary wins, we need to multiply each of these pairs together, then sum. MATLAB does this by matrix multiplication of the row vector *pm* by the column matrix *pb'* , which is the transpose of *pb* . Thus,

_____ MATLAB Script _____

```
>> P = pm*pb'                    % operation to multiply pairs and sum
   P = 0.2738                    % the result
```

As an alternative, if we are not interested in the intermediate details, we could bypass the separate calculations and the display and simply give the MATLAB command:

_____ MATLAB Script _____

```
>> P = cbinom(10,0.8,1:10)*ibinom(10,0.85,0:9)'
   P = 0.2738
```

Modification of the problem: It is not necessary that Bill and Mary have the same number of free throws. In a well-intended, but perhaps not appreciated gesture, Bill allows Mary to have one extra free throw. The formal structure is the same as before except that $n = 10$ is replaced by $n = 11$ for Mary and Bill can make all ten free throws. Thus,

_____ MATLAB Script _____

```
>> pm = cbinom(11,0.8,1:11);     % cumulative probabilities for Mary
>> pb = ibinom(10,0.85,0:10);    % individual probabilities for Bill
>> P = pm*pb'                    % operation to multiply pairs and sum
   P = 0.4559                    % result
```

Note that Mary's chances of winning have increased considerably, but the advantage is still Bill's.

A number of variations of these patterns provide useful application models. Some alternatives and extensions for the basketball problem are included in the Exploration Problems for this chapter. Also, these problems can be formulated and treated as problems of independent random variables. For examples, see the Exploration Problems for Chapter 5.

─────────●

REINFORCEMENT EXERCISES AND EXPLORATION PROBLEMS

─────────■───────

REINFORCEMENT EXERCISES

P2.1. A certain type of failure in a system may have one of ten causes. If E is the event of the failure and A_i is the event of the ith cause, experience indicates the following data:

$$PEA = [0.22\ 0.05\ 0.68\ 0.68\ 0.93\ 0.38\ 0.52\ 0.83\ 0.03\ 0.05]$$
$$PA = [0.05\ 0.02\ 0.18\ 0.08\ 0.24\ 0.18\ 0.15\ 0.05\ 0.01\ 0.04]$$

PEA is the matrix whose elements are $P(E \mid A_i)$ and *PA* is the matrix whose elements are $P(A_i)$. If a failure occurs, determine the conditional probability of each cause.

P2.2. Use the procedure freq to sort and count frequencies in the following list:

$$2\ 0\ 7\ 7\ 9\ 4\ 5\ 8\ 0\ 1\ 5\ 7\ 0\ \cdots$$
$$4\ 1\ 4\ 7\ 6\ 9\ 8\ 5\ 1\ 7\ 4\ 6$$

Try other such lists.

P2.3. The class $\{A, B, C, D\}$ is independent with respective probabilities 0.35, 0.77, 0.43, and 0.62. Use minprob to obtain the minterm probabilities. Use the function minmap to put them in a 4 by 4 table corresponding to the minterm map convention we use.

P2.4. Minterm probabilities $p(0)$ through $p(15)$ for the class $\{A, B, C, D\}$ are, in order,

$$0.084\ 0.196\ 0.036\ 0.084\ 0.085\ 0.196\ 0.035\ 0.084\ \cdots$$
$$0.021\ 0.049\ 0.009\ 0.021\ 0.020\ 0.049\ 0.010\ 0.021$$

Use the function imintest to show whether or not the class $\{A, B, C, D\}$ is independent. Repeat for minterm probabilities produced by mincalc for problems in Chapter 1. Also, use imintest on minterm probabilities produced by minprob.

P2.5. A company has three task forces trying to produce a new device by a certain deadline. The groups work independently, with respective probabilities 0.8, 0.9, and 0.75 of completing on time. What is the probability that at least one group completes on time?

P2.6. David, Mary, Joan, Hal, and Wayne take an exam in their probability course. Their probabilities of making 90 percent or more are 0.72, 0.83, 0.75, 0.92, and 0.65, respectively. Assume these are independent events. What is the probability three or more make grades of at least 90 percent?

P2.7. A basketball player takes ten free throws in a contest. On her first shot she is nervous and has probability 0.3 of making the shot. She begins to settle down and probabilities on the next seven shots are 0.5, 0.6, 0.7, 0.8, 0.8, 0.8, and 0.85, respectively. Then she realizes her opponent is doing well and becomes tense as she takes the last two shots, with probabilities reduced to 0.75, 0.65. Assuming independence between the shots, what is the probability she will make k or more for $k = 2, 3, \cdots, 10$?

P2.8. A system has five components which fail independently. Their respective reliabilities are 0.95, 0.90, 0.77, 0.85, and 0.91. Units 1 and 2 operate as a "series" subsystem. Units 3, 4, and 5 comprise a 2 of 3 subsystem (i.e., the subsystem operates iff 2 or more of the 3 are operative). The two subsystems operate in "parallel" to comprise the complete system. What is the system reliability?

P2.9. A device has five sensors connected to an alarm system. The alarm is given if three or more of the sensors trigger a switch. If a dangerous condition is present, each of the switches has high (but not unit) probability of activating; if the dangerous condition does not exist, each of the switches has low (but not zero) probability of activating (falsely). Suppose D = the event of the dangerous condition and A = the event the alarm is activated. Proper operation consists of $AD \uplus A^c D^c$.

Suppose E_i = the event the ith unit is activated. Since the switches operate independently, we suppose

$$\{E_1, E_2, E_3, E_4, E_5\} \text{ ci } |D \quad \text{and} \quad \text{ci } |D^c$$

Assume the conditional probabilities of the E_i, given D, are 0.91, 0.93, 0.96, 0.87, and 0.97 and given D^c are 0.03, 0.02, 0.07, 0.04, and 0.01, respectively. If $P(D) = 0.02$, what is the probability the alarm system acts properly? *Suggestion:* use the conditional independence and the procedure ckn.

P2.10. A physician thinks the odds are about 2 to 1 that a patient has a certain disease. He seeks the "independent" advice of three specialists. Let H be the event the disease is present, and A, B, and C be the events the respective consultants agree this is the case. The physician decides to go with the majority. Since the advisers act in an operationally independent manner, it seems reasonable to suppose $\{A, B, C\}$ ci $|H$ and ci $|H^c$. Experience indicates

$$P(A\,|\,H) = 0.8, \qquad P(B\,|\,H) = 0.7, \qquad P(C\,|\,H) = 0.75$$
$$P(A^c\,|\,H^c) = 0.85, \qquad P(B^c\,|\,H^c) = 0.8, \qquad P(C^c\,|\,H^c) = 0.7$$

What is the probability of the right decision (i.e., he treats the disease if present and does not if the disease is not present)?

P2.11. A sample of 150 subjects is taken from a population which has two subgroups. The subgroup membership of each subject in the sample is known. Each one is asked a battery of ten questions designed to be independent, in the sense that the answer to any one is not affected by the answer to any other. The subjects answer independently. Data on the results are summarized in the following table:

Q	GROUP 1 (83 members)			GROUP 2 (67 members)		
	Yes	No	Unc.	Yes	No	Unc.
1	61	17	5	28	34	5
2	29	20	34	51	14	2
3	58	13	12	35	24	8
4	41	36	6	54	9	4
5	78	4	1	11	37	19
6	31	34	18	41	19	7
7	48	28	7	15	28	24
8	54	8	21	18	38	11
9	72	8	3	17	30	20
10	53	19	11	43	17	7

Check the classification for the following profiles for persons selected at random:

$$[Y, N, Y, N, Y, U, N, U, Y, U]$$
$$[N, N, U, N, Y, Y, U, N, N, Y]$$
$$[Y, Y, N, Y, U, U, N, N, Y, Y]$$

Try other profiles. See if you can guess the classification before processing.

P2.12. There are 100 random digits, 0 through 9, with each possible digit equally likely on each choice. What is the probability that eleven or more are zeros?

P2.13. Only thirty percent of the items from a production line meet stringent requirements for a special job. Units from the line are tested in succession. Under the usual assumptions for Bernoulli trials, what is the probability that three satisfactory units will be found in eight or fewer trials?

P2.14. The probability is 0.02 that a virus will survive application of a certain vaccine. What is the probability that of a batch of 500 viruses, ten or more will survive treatment?

P2.15. In a shipment of 20,000 items, 400 are defective. These are scattered randomly throughout the entire lot. Assume the probability of a defective item is the same on each choice. What is the probability that:

a. At least one will appear in a random sample of 35?
b. At most five will appear in a random sample of 50?

P2.16. A device has probability p of operating successfully on any trial in a sequence. What probability p is necessary to ensure that the probability of successes on each of the first four trials is 0.93? With that value of p, what is the probability of four or more successes in five trials?

P2.17. A survey form is sent to 100 persons. If they decide independently whether or not to reply and each has probability 1/4 of replying, then what is the probability of k or more replies, where $k = 15, 20, 25, 30, 35,$ or 40?

P2.18. Ten numbers are produced by a random number generator. What is the probability four or more are less than or equal to 0.56?

P2.19. A player rolls a pair of dice five times. She scores a "hit" on any throw if she gets a 6 or 7. She wins iff she scores an *odd* number of hits in the five throws. What is the probability she wins on any sequence of five throws? Suppose she plays the game 20 consecutive times. What is the probability she wins at least 10 times? What is the probability she wins more than half the time in the 20 games?

P2.20. A racetrack regular claims he can pick the winning horse in any race 90 percent of the time. In order to test his claim, he picks a horse to win in each of ten races. Consider the trials to constitute a Bernoulli sequence.

a. What is the probability of picking at least nine correctly if his probability of success is the claimed 0.90?
b. Suppose the player is really guessing, and he picks at random from the five horses in each race. What is the probability he will pick correctly in at least half of the races?

P2.21. Two salesmen work differently. Ed spends more time with his customers than Frank and hence tends to see fewer customers. On a given day Ed sees five customers and Frank sees six. The customers make decisions independently. If the probabilities for success with Ed's customers are 0.7, 0.8, 0.8, 0.6, and 0.7 and the probabilities for success with Frank's customers are 0.6, 0.5, 0.4, 0.6, 0.6, and 0.4, then what is the probability Ed makes more sales than Frank? What is the probability that Ed will make three or more sales? What is the probability that Frank will make three or more sales?

P2.22. Two teams of students take a probability exam. The entire group performs individually and independently. Team 1 has five members and Team 2 has six members. They have the following individual probabilities of making an "A" on the exam.

Team 1: 0.83 0.87 0.92 0.77 0.86

Team 2: 0.68 0.91 0.74 0.68 0.73 0.83

a. What is the probability Team 1 will make *at least as many* "A" 's as Team 2?
b. What is the probability Team 1 will make *more* "A" 's than Team 2?

EXPLORATION PROBLEMS

P2.1. Consider the basketball freethrow competition between Mary and Bill. Is there an optimum number of throws for Mary? Can you suggest a reason why? Since there is no reasonable analytical way to determine an optimum, search for one experimentally by solving the problem for different values of n.

P2.2. Set up other compound Bernoulli trials with other numbers of trials and other success probabilities. Are there optimum numbers of trials for different probability pairs? Are there any patterns evident? Can you suggest reasons for these patterns?

P2.3. Suppose there were "learning" or adjustment as the trials proceed. Then the probabilities would increase with the number of trials, although independence would be a reasonable assumption. Try some reasonable probabilities and use ikn and ckn. How do results vary with the number of trials?

P2.4. Suppose a set of minterm probabilities were given. Try modifying the function ikn to determine the probability of k of n successes in this case. *Note* that this case can be determined using the procedure canonical (see problems for Chapter 4).

P2.5 The Law of Large Numbers. Use the procedures btdata and bt to set up a random sequence for $n = 1000$, then use the following MATLAB procedure:

———————————— MATLAB Script ————————————

```
N = 1:n;
f = cumsum(B')./N;   % Relative frequences for each k, 1
<= k <= n.
semilogx(N,f)        % Plot with logarithmic x-scale
```

By using the hold command, two or more sequences can be compared, to show the differences for individual sequences but the convergences to the same limit.

Random Variables
and Distributions

PREVIEW

MATLAB functions are developed to calculate the probabilities for several discrete and continuous probability distributions. Although a great variety of distributions may be encountered in practice, those selected are particularly useful. They are introduced and utilized in most textbooks on probability.

1. REVIEW OF CONCEPTS AND NOTATION

A real *random variable* X describes a quantity associated with the outcomes of the basic trial. For each elementary outcome ω there corresponds a number $t = X(\omega)$. Thus, X is a *function* defined on the basic space Ω. The function X, as a mapping from Ω to the real line $\mathbf{R}$, induces a *probability distribution* on the subsets of the line. An *event* determined by X is the set of those ω for which $X(\omega)$ is one of a prescribed set of values. For example,

1. The event that X is less than or equal to 10 is the set $\{\omega: X(\omega) \leq 10\}$, abbreviated $\{X \leq 10\}$.
2. The event that X is greater than -2 and no greater than 4 is the set

$$\{\omega: -2 < X(\omega) \leq 4\} = \{-2 < X \leq 4\} = \{X \in (-2, 4]\}$$

Now the probability that X is less than or equal to 10 is the probability mass associated with the event $\{X \leq 10\}$, and the probability that X is greater than -2 and no greater than 4 is the probability mass associated with the event $\{X \in (-2, 4]\}$. The induced probability distribution can be described in equivalent ways:

1. The assignment of probability mass to each interval M by the rule $P(X \in M)$ determines a probability measure P_X on the subsets of the real line such that $P_X(M) = P(X \in M)$. The function P_X on subsets of the real line is a new probability measure. Its basic space is the real line $\mathbf{R}$ and subsets M of real numbers play the role of events.

2. A *probability distribution function* F_X is defined by $F_X(t) = P(X \le t)$ for each real t. That is, $F_X(t)$ is the probability mass at or to the left of point t on the real line. The probability distribution is described completely by its distribution function. Properties of distribution functions are well-known and easily visualized in terms of the mass distribution on the line. Thus, F_X is nondecreasing, going from zero to one as t increases from the smallest value to the largest value taken on by X. If $P(X = t_0) = p_0 > 0$, then there is probability mass p_0 concentrated at $t = t_0$, and the graph of F_X has a jump discontinuity of height p_0 at that point. Otherwise, F_X is continuous.

   a. If X takes on only a discrete set of values, F_X is a step function with step increases at each value t_i in the amount of the probability $p_i = P(X = t_i)$.

   b. If X has no point mass concentrations, then in any practical case there is a *probability density function* f_X with the property that

   $$P(X \in M) = \int_M f_x(u)\, du, \quad \text{where } M \text{ is the region of integration}$$

   In this case, $F_X(t) = \int_{-\infty}^{t} f_X(u)\, du$ and $f_X(t) = F_X'(t)$, the derivative of F_X at t. Distributions with a density are called *absolutely continuous,* or simply continuous.

The probability distribution determines the "behavior" of a random variable. Two random variables with the same distribution have the same probability of taking on any given set of values. This does not mean, however, that the two random variables are the same. It is easy to construct examples of random variables which have the same distribution but are never equal (i.e., do not take on the same value on any trial).

2. MATLAB FUNCTIONS FOR SOME DISCRETE DISTRIBUTIONS

We consider several distributions which are employed frequently in applications. For some, ordinary MATLAB functions suffice for calculations. For others, we have developed user defined functions.

BINOMIAL COEFFICIENTS

The binomial coefficient $C(n, k) = \frac{n!}{k!\,(n-k)!}$ $0 \leq k \leq n$. The following user defined function may be employed.

_____ MATLAB Script _____

```
function y=comb(n,k)
% Computes binomial coefficients C(n,k)
% Version of 12/10/92
% k may be a matrix of integers between 0 and n
% result y is a matrix of the same dimensions
y = round(gamma(n+1)./(gamma(k + 1).*gamma(n + 1 - k)));
```

SIMPLE RANDOM VARIABLES

A simple random variable is one which takes on a finite set of distinct values, say $\{t_1, t_2, \cdots, t_n\}$, with probabilities $p_i = P(X = t_i)$ $1 \leq i \leq n$. The distribution is often best represented by a list of values and a list of corresponding probabilities. In MATLAB, we usually employ row matrices

$$t = [t_1 \; t_2 \; \cdots \; t_n] \quad \text{and} \quad p = [p_1 \; p_2 \; \cdots \; p_n]$$

When entered in the MATLAB workspace as matrices with designated symbols, these may be used directly in the calculations.

BINOMIAL DISTRIBUTION

In the treatment of Bernoulli trials in Chapter 2, we encounter the binomial (n, p) distribution as the distribution of the random variable S_n, which counts the number of successes in a sequence of n Bernoulli trials with probability p of success on any trial. In that treatment, we illustrate the use of the two functions *ibinom* and *cbinom* for calculating individual and cumulative terms, $P(S_n = k)$ and $P(S_n \geq k)$, respectively.

$$P(S_n = k) = C(n, k)p^k(1 - p)^{n-k} \quad \text{and}$$

$$P(S_n \geq k) = \sum_{r=k}^{n} P(S_n = r) \quad 0 \leq k \leq n$$

For the MATLAB procedures, we use a modification of a computation strategy employed by S. Weintraub: *Tables of the Cumulative Binomial Probability Distribution for Small Values of p*, 1963. The book contains a particularly helpful error analysis, written by Leo J. Cohen. Experimentation with sums and expectations indicates a precision for ibinom and cbinom MATLAB calculations that is better than 10^{-10} for $n = 1000$ and p from 0.01 to 0.99. A similar precision holds for values of n up to 5000, provided np or nq are limited to approximately 500. Above this value for np or nq, the computations break down.

```
function y=ibinom(n,p,k)
% Individual binomial probabilities
% Version of 10/5/93
% n a positive integer;  p a probability
% k a row vector of integers between 0 and n
% y = P(X>=k) (a row vector of probabilities)
if p > 0.5
a = [1 ((1-p)/p)*ones(1,n)];
b = [1 n:-1:1];
c = [1 1:n];
br = (p^n)*cumprod(a.*b./c);
bi = fliplr(br);
else
a = [1 (p/(1-p))*ones(1,n)];
b = [1 n:-1:1];
c = [1 1:n];
bi = ((1-p)^n)*cumprod(a.*b./c);
end
y = bi(k+1);
```

```
function y=cbinom(n,p,k)
% Cumulative binomial distribution
% Version of 10/5/93
% n a positive integer;  p a probability
% k a row vector of integers between 0 and n
% y = P((X>=k) (a row vector of probabilities)
if p > 0.5
a = [1 ((1-p)/p)*ones(1,n)];
b = [1 n:-1:1];
c = [1 1:n];
br = (p^n)*cumprod(a.*b./c);
bcr = cumsum(br);
bc = fliplr(bcr);
else
a = [1 (p/(1-p))*ones(1,n)];
b = [1 n:-1:1];
c = [1 1:n];
bi = ((1-p)^n)*cumprod(a.*b./c);
b = cumsum(bi);
bc = [1 1-b(1:n)];
end
y = bc(k+1);
```

CHAPTER 3

GEOMETRIC DISTRIBUTION

The geometric distribution is related to Bernoulli sequences. There are, in fact, two closely related random variables which are referred to as having the geometric distribution.

1. The random variable X which counts the number of failures before the first success. This is sometimes called the *waiting time* to the first success.

$$P(X = k) = pq^k \qquad 0 \leq k \quad \text{where } q = 1 - p$$

2. The random variable Y which designates the number of the trial on which the first success is realized. This is sometimes called the *time* of the first success.

$$P(Y = k) = pq^{k-1} \qquad 1 \leq k \quad \text{where } q = 1 - p$$

The random variables are related by $X = Y - 1$. Although usage varies among authors, we choose to refer to the distribution for X as the geometric distribution and indicate this by $X \sim$ geometric (p). We then say $Y - 1 \sim$ geometric (p) to designate the other distribution.

There is no need for a special user defined program for the geometric distribution, since we are only raising q to integer powers for individual probabilities, and $P(X \geq m) = q^m$.

EXAMPLE 3.1 Suppose $X \sim$ geometric (0.37). Determine the probability X takes on the values $3, 9, 17$.

---------------------- MATLAB Script ----------------------

```
>> p = 0.37;
>> q = 1 - p;
>> k = [3 9 17];
>> PX = p*(q.^k)
PX =      0.0925     0.0058     0.0001 % Values are in workspace
>> disp([k;PX]')                        % Display
    3.0000    0.0925
    9.0000    0.0058
   17.0000    0.0001
```

NEGATIVE BINOMIAL DISTRIBUTION

The negative binomial (or Pascal) distribution is also related to Bernoulli sequences. As in the geometric distribution case, there are two related distributions called negative binomial. The random variable X_m counts the number of failures in a Bernoulli sequence before the mth success. The random variable Y_m designates the number of the trial on which the mth success occurs. It should be apparent that for $m = 1$ we have the geometric distribution (in the two alternative forms).

The user defined MATLAB function below calculates the individual probabilities for the random variable Y_m whose value is the number of the trial on which the mth success occurs. Elementary considerations show that

$$P(Y_m = k) = C(k - 1, m - 1)p^m q^{k-m}, \qquad k \geq m \quad q = 1 - p$$

_____ MATLAB Script _____

```
function  y=nbinom(m,p,k)
% Probability the mth success occurs on the kth trial
% Version of 12/10/92
% m a positive integer;  p a probability
% k a matrix of integers greater than or equal to m
% y = P(X=k) (a matrix of the same dimensions as k)
q = 1 - p;
y = ((p^m)/gamma(m)).*(q.^(k - m)).*gamma(k)./gamma(k - m + 1);
```

EXAMPLE 3.2   In a Bernoulli sequence with probability $p = 0.43$ of success on any trial, what is the probability the third success comes no later than the seventh trial?

Solution   _____ MATLAB Script _____

```
>> PI = nbinom(3,0.43,3:7)   % Individual probabilities
PI =   0.0795 0.1360    0.1550    0.1472    0.1259
>> P = sum(PI)
P   =   0.6436                    % P(Y3 <= 7)
```

WHAT IF?   Suppose only cumulative binomial probabilities could be obtained. Could this problem be solved in these terms? If the third success comes before the seventh trial, what does this imply about S_7, the number of successes in 7 trials? Note that

$$P(Y_m \leq k) = P(S_k \geq m)$$

From this fact derive an expression for $P(Y_m = k)$ in terms of the cumulative binomial distribution. Calculate $P(Y_3 = 7)$ with nbinom for the case above. Next, calculate the same probability with cbinom. ∎

THE POISSON DISTRIBUTION

Random variable X has the Poisson distribution with parameter μ, designated $N \sim \text{Poisson}\ (\mu)$, iff it takes on nonnegative integer values with probability

$$P(N = k) = e^{-\mu}\frac{\mu^k}{k!} \qquad 0 \le k$$

The Poisson distribution appears in several natural ways in applications.

1. It appears as an approximation to the binomial distribution. Suppose $X \sim \text{binomial}\ (n, p)$. If n is large and p is small enough that the Poisson (np) distribution may be calculated, a simple limit argument (cf *PA*, Section 8.2) shows that X is approximately Poisson (np); that is, the parameter $\mu = np$. This is particularly useful if tables of the binomial distribution must be used, since they may limit the permissible values of n too severely for the problem at hand.
2. In the following discussion of the gamma distribution, the relationship between the gamma and the Poisson distributions is noted. The Poisson distribution is discrete, while the gamma distribution is continuous. It is frequently expedient to utilize a Poisson table or to calculate a few terms with a scientific hand calculator.
3. Random variables with the Poisson distribution serve as "counting functions" in a variety of applications. The discussion of the "Poisson Counting Process" section in Chapter 7 shows that this role is often a result of the relationship between the Poisson distribution and the gamma distribution.

As in the case of the binomial distribution, we have a function for the individual terms and one for the cumulative case. The procedures employed use a computational strategy similar to that used for the binomial case. Not only does this work for large μ, but the precision is at least as good as that for the binomial procedures. Experience indicates that the procedure is good for $\mu \le 700$. It breaks down at about 710, largely because of limitations of the MATLAB exponential function.

──────────── MATLAB Script ────────────

```
function y=ipoisson(m,k)
% calculates individual Poisson probabilities
% Version of 10/15/93
% mu = mean value
% k may be a row or column vector of integer values
% y = P(X = k) (a row vector of probabilities)
K = max(k);
p = exp(-mu)*cumprod([1 mu*ones(1,K)]./[1 1:K]);
y = p(k+1);
```

```
function y=cpoisson(m,n)
% Cumulative Poisson probabilities
% Version of 10/15/93
% m = mean value mu
& k may be a row or column vector of integer values
% y = P(X >= k) (a row vector of probabilities)
K = max(k);
p = exp(-mu)*cumprod([1 mu*ones(1,K)]./[1 1:K]);
pc = [1 1 - cumsum(p)];
y = pc(k+1);
```

EXAMPLE 3.3

Noise Pulses

The number N of noise pulses of more than 300 volts arriving on a transmission line in an hour has Poisson (30) distribution. What is the probability that in the hour there will be 25 or more noise pulses of 300 or more volts? What is the probability of at least 25 and not more than 35 of these in that time?

For the second question, we note that $P(25 \le N \le 35) = P(N \ge 25) - P(N \ge 36)$. The first term on the right-hand side is the sum of all p_k from 25 on, and the second is the sum of all the p_k from 36 on. The difference leaves the sum of the desired terms.

Solution

MATLAB Script

```
>> P1 = cpoisson(30,25)
P1 = 0.8428
>> P2 = cpoisson(30,25) - cpoisson(30,36)
P2 = 0.6854
% An alternate solution
>> P = cpoisson(30,[25 36])    % Calculates both terms at the same time
P =   0.8428    0.1574
>> P1 = P(1)                   % Select the first term for first question
P1 = 0.8428
>> P2 = P(1) -P(2)             % Take difference for second question
P2 = 0.6854
```

EXAMPLE 3.4

Poisson Approximation to the Binomial

Two percent of the items purchased in bulk from a supplier are defective. The items are packaged in lots of 500 by the retailer. The retailer guarantees that not more than 20 in any package will be defective. What is the probability the guarantee is satisfied?

Solution

Let D be the random quantity which is the number of defective items in a package. Then we may take D to be binomial $(500, 0.02)$. $P(D \le 20) =$

$1 - P(D \geq 21)$. We first calculate with cbinomial then we compare with the Poisson approximation.

—————————— MATLAB Script ——————————

```
>> PD2 = 1 - cbinomial(500,0.02, 21)
PD2 = 0.9986
>> % Poisson approximation
>> np = 0.02*500;
>> pD2 = 1 - cpoisson(np,21)
pD2 = 0.9984              % The agreement is quite good
```

3. MATLAB FUNCTIONS FOR SOME CONTINUOUS DISTRIBUTIONS

The following functions calculate probabilities for some important absolutely continuous distributions. There are other commonly used distributions (e.g., the uniform and the exponential) for which there is no need for special user defined functions.

THE GAMMA DISTRIBUTION

We say random variable X is gamma (α, λ, t) iff it has density function

$$f_X(t) = \frac{\lambda^\alpha t^{\alpha-1} e^{-\lambda t}}{\Gamma(\alpha)} \qquad t \geq 0$$

The integral for determining the distribution function utilizes the *incomplete gamma function*. As a result, a suitable user defined MATLAB function is:

—————————— MATLAB Script ——————————

```
function y-gammadbn(alpha,lambda,t)
% Distribution function for X ~ gamma (alpha, lambda)
% Version of 12/10/92   (A modification is needed for MATLAB v3.5)
% alpha, lambda positive parameters
% t may be a matrix of positive numbers
% y = P(X<= t) (a matrix of the same dimensions as t)
y = gammainc(lambda*t, alpha);
```

The integral of the density function is the incomplete gamma function. For $\alpha = n$, a positive integer, this may be expressed as a sum of exponential terms (see a table of integrals). A careful examination of this representation shows the following connection between the Poisson and gamma distributions for the case $\alpha = n$:

1. If $X \sim$ gamma (n, λ), then $P(X \leq t) = P(Y \geq n)$, where $Y \sim$ Poisson (λt), $t > 0$.
2. If $Y \sim$ Poisson (λt), then $P(Y \geq n) = P(X \leq t)$, where $X \sim$ gamma (n, λ).

EXAMPLE 3.5
Poisson and Gamma Distributions

The sum of times to failure (in hundreds of hours) for five independent random units is a random quantity $X \sim$ gamma $(5, 0.15)$. Determine the probability $P(X \leq 25)$.

Solution

$P(X \leq 25) = P(Y \geq 5)$, where $Y \sim$ Poisson $(\mu = 25 \times 0.15 = 3.75)$. We compare three solutions: direct calculation with gammadbn, calculation with cpoisson, and simple calculation of the necessary terms.

1. $P(X \leq 25)$: P = gammadbn(5,0.15,25) = 0.3225
2. $P(Y \geq 5)$:   P = cpoisson(3.75,5) v 0.3225
3. $P(Y \geq 5) = 1 - (p_0 + p_1 + p_2 + p_3 + p_4)$

$$= 1 - e^{-3.75}\left(1 + 3.75 + \frac{3.75^2}{2} + \frac{3.75^3}{6} + \frac{3.75^4}{24}\right)$$

$$= 0.3225$$

THE NORMAL DISTRIBUTION

We say random variable X has the normal (or Gaussian) distribution with parameters (μ, σ^2), often designated $X \sim N(\mu, \sigma^2)$, iff it has the density function

$$f_X(t) = \frac{1}{\sigma\sqrt{2\pi}}\, \exp\left(-\frac{1}{2}\left(\frac{t - \mu}{\sigma}\right)^2\right) \quad \forall\, t$$

The parameter μ is the mean value and σ^2 is the variance. This is one of the most commonly encountered distributions in probability. Unfortunately, the integral of the density function cannot be expressed in terms of elementary functions. It is necessary to utilize numerical methods of integration. Extensive tables are available. It is always possible to express the distribution function $F_X(t)$, for any parameter values, in terms of the standardized distribution function for the case $\mu = 0$ and $\sigma^2 = 1$. Use of the MATLAB function below does not require this standardization by the user, since it is incorporated into the procedure.

```
function y=gaussian(m,v,t)
% Distribution function for X ~ N(m, v)
% Version of 11/18/92 (A modification is needed for MATLAB v3.5)
% m = mean, v = variance
% t is a matrix of evaluation points
% y = P(X<=t) (a matrix of the same dimensions as t)
u = (t - m)./sqrt(2*v);
if u >= 0
        y = 0.5*(erf(u) + 1);
else
        y = 0.5*erfc(-u);
end
```

●————————

EXAMPLE 3.6
Gaussian
Probabilities

$X \sim N(12, 4)$. Determine $P(9 \le X \le 13)$.

_____ MATLAB Script _____

```
>> a = gaussian(12,4,[9 13])
a = 0.0668      0.6915
>> p = a(2) - a(1)
p = 0.6247
```

The role of the gaussian distribution in probability is largely due to a family of theorems known generically as the *central limit theorem*. Under various conditions commonly met in practice, the sum of a sufficiently large number of independent random variables is a random variable which is approximately normally distributed. This has important implications for the binomial, Poisson, and gamma distributions.

1. The binomial distribution is the distribution for the number of successes in n Bernoulli trials. As such, it is the sum of the indicator functions I_{E_i} for a success on the ith trial in the sequence. If n is large, the sum of the n independent random variables is approximately normally distributed. Since $E[S_n] = np$ and $\text{Var}[S_n] = npq$, for large n, S_n is approximately $N(np, npq)$.

2. We note above that for large n and small p, the binomial (n, p) distribution is approximately Poisson (np). Hence, the Poisson distribution should be approximately $N(np, np)$, which for small p is approximately $N(np, npq)$.

3. Since the gamma (n, λ) distribution can be expressed in terms of the Poisson distribution, it can therefore be expressed approximately in terms of the gaussian distribution.

MATLAB FUNCTIONS FOR SOME CONTINUOUS DISTRIBUTIONS

THE BETA DISTRIBUTION

Random variable X has the beta distribution with parameters (r, s), $r > 0$, $s > 0$, designated $X \sim$ beta (r, s), iff it has density function

$$f_X(t) = \frac{\Gamma(r)\Gamma(s)}{\Gamma(r + s)} \, t^{r-1}(1 - t)^{s-1} \qquad 0 < t < 1, \; r > 0, \; s > 0$$

This distribution, which has range $[0, 1]$, is used widely as an empirical distribution in decision processes. By varying the parameters, a variety of shapes of density functions over the unit interval can be achieved. Shifting and changing scale on the argument makes it possible to approximate many densities on any bounded interval. Figure 3.1 shows plots of the beta density function for $r = 2$ and $s = 1, 2, 10$. Figure 3.2 shows plots for $r = 5$ and $s = 2, 5, 10$. If $s < 1$, the density has a vertical asymptote at $t = 1$; if $r < 1$, there is a vertical asymptote at $t = 0$. For $r = s = 1$, the density has the constant value one, corresponding to uniform density on $[0, 1]$.

We have two MATLAB programs. The first calculates values of the density function, which is used to generate curves such as those shown in Figures 3.1 and 3.2.

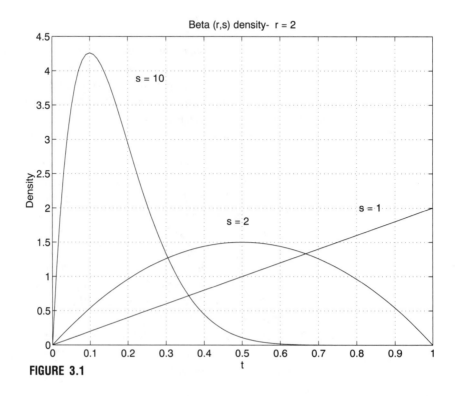

FIGURE 3.1

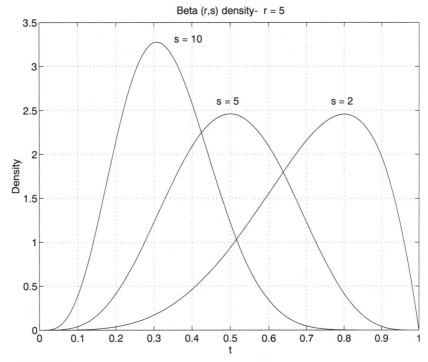

FIGURE 3.2

_____ MATLAB Script _____

```
function y=beta(r,s,t)
% Density function for Beta (r,s) distribution
% Version of 8/5/93
% t is a matrix of evaluation points between 0 and 1
% y is a matrix of the same dimensions as t
y = (gamma(r+s)/(gamma(r)*gamma(s)))*(t.^(r-1).*(1-t).^(s-1));
```

The second MATLAB function is used to determine the distribution function for X. It employs the MATLAB function betainc for the incomplete beta function. We have simply renamed the function and changed the order of parameters to be consistent with our usage elsewhere.

_____ MATLAB Script _____

```
function y=betadbn(r,s,t)
% Distribution function for X  beta(r,s)
% Version of 7/27/93
% y = P(X<=t) (a matrix of the same dimensions as t)
y = betainc(t,r,s);
```

THE WEIBULL DISTRIBUTION

Random variable X has the Weibull distribution with parameters (α, λ, ν), designated $X \sim$ Weibull (α, λ, ν), iff it has density function

$$f_X(t) = \alpha\lambda(t - \nu)^{\alpha-1}e^{-\lambda(t-\nu)^{\alpha}} \quad t \geq \nu \quad \text{(and zero elsewhere)}$$

The parameter ν is a shift parameter, appearing in the expression in the combination $t - \nu$. We consider only the case $\nu = 0$. With $\nu = 0$, this distribution is essentially the exponential (λ) distribution with a distorted time scale. It reduces to the exponential case when $\alpha = 1$. It is widely used in approximating empirical densities in reliability theory. Figures 3.3 and 3.4 show representative shapes for various combinations of α and λ.

We have two MATLAB functions, one for the density and one for the distribution function. Only the case $\nu = 0$ is programmed.

—————————————— MATLAB Script ——————————————

```
function y=weibull(alpha,lambda,t)
% Density function for Weibull (alpha, lambda, 0) distribution
% Version of 1/24/91
% t is a matrix of positive evaluation points
% y is a matrix of the same dimensions as t
y = alpha*lambda*(t.^(alpha - 1)).*exp(-lambda*t.^alpha);
```

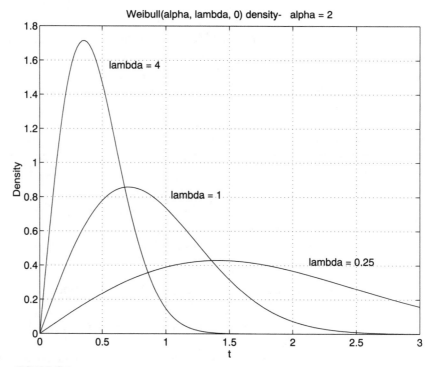

FIGURE 3.3

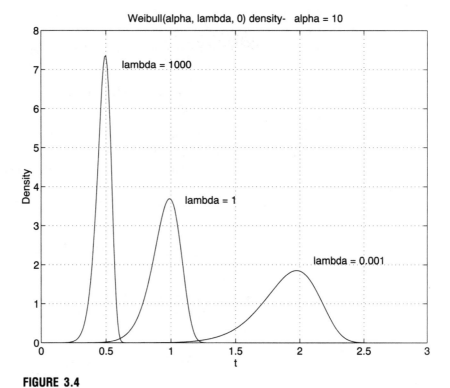

Weibull(alpha, lambda, 0) density- alpha = 10

FIGURE 3.4

_____ MATLAB Script _____

```
function y=weibulld(alpha,lambda,t)
% Distribution function for X ~ Weibull (alpha, lambda, 0)
% Version of 1/24/91
% t is a matrix of positive evaluation points
% y = P(X<=t) (a matrix of the same dimensions as t)
y = 1 - exp(-lambda*t.^alpha);
```

4. THE MULTINOMIAL DISTRIBUTION

■

We consider a generalization of the Bernoulli trial model. In this case, we have a sequence of independent success-failure trials. The outcome of each trial is one of two kinds: a "success" or a "failure." In the multinomial case, we suppose there are N trials, each of which has an outcome of one of m types. Let E_{ki} = the event the ith trial produces a result of the kth type. The random variable whose value is the type of the ith result may be expressed

$$T_i = \sum_{k=1}^{m} k I_{E_{ki}} \qquad 1 \le i \le N$$

Note that for each i, the class $\{E_{ki}: 1 \leq k \leq m\}$ is a partition, since on each trial the outcome is exactly one of these types. We assume successive outcomes are independent and the probability for each type remains invariant with i. Specifically, we assume

1. $\{T_i: 1 \leq i \leq N\}$ is an independent class.
2. $P(E_{ki}) = P(T_i = k) = p_k$ $1 \leq k \leq m$, invariant with i.

If N_k is the number of outcomes of type k, then $N_k = \sum_{i=1}^{N} I_{E_{ki}}$. The assumptions ensure that $N_k \sim$ binomial (N, p_k) $1 \leq k \leq m$. For $m = 2$, we have the Bernoulli case, with one type a success and the other type a failure. If B_r is the number of types for which there are exactly r results in N trials and if D_r is the number of types for which there are r or more results in N trials, then

$$B_r = \sum_{k=1}^{m} I_{\{N_k = r\}} \quad \text{and} \quad D_r = \sum_{k=1}^{m} I_{\{N_k \geq r\}}$$

Since $N_1 + N_2 + \cdots + N_m = N$, the N_k do not form an independent class. Thus, obtaining distributions for B_r and D_r may be quite difficult, except for small N and m, or in very special cases. However, because of linearity, the expectations are simply

$$E[B_r] = \sum_{k=1}^{m} P(N_k = r) \quad \text{and} \quad E[D_r] = \sum_{k=1}^{m} P(N_k \geq r)$$

EXAMPLE 3.7
Candy Problem

A very large container of hard candies has 23 percent red, 30 percent green, 25 percent yellow, and 22 percent purple candies. These are mixed thoroughly. One hundred pieces are chosen at random, so that the probability that any choice yields red is 0.23, etc. The choices may be considered independent, with probabilities the same on each selection.

(a) What is the probability of selecting 25 or more red?
(b) What is the expected number of colors for which there are 25 or more selected?

Solution

(a) If N_1 is the number of red, then $N_1 \sim$ binomial $(100, 0.23)$. Use of the function cbinom gives $P(N_1 \geq 25) = 0.3539$.
(b) A MATLAB solution for the second part is

—————————— MATLAB Script ——————————

```
>> P = [0.23 0.30 0.25 0.22];
>> for i = 1:4
 p(i) = cbinom(100,P(i),25);
end
>> E20 = sum(p)
E20 =   2.0471
```

Since the N_k do not form an independent class, the task of calculating joint probabilities is in general quite difficult. For a single point, a well-known result gives

$$P(N_1 = n_1, N_2 = n_2, \cdots N_m = n_m) \;=\; N! \prod_{k=1}^{m} \frac{p_k^{n_k}}{n_k!}$$

$$\text{provided } n_1 + n_2 + \cdots + n_m = N$$

This expression is somewhat cumbersome to use for more than one point.

The following MATLAB procedure works well for small N and m. The principal limitation on size is the amount of memory available. The procedure generates all possible strings of the m types of length N. Also, for each string of types it generates a companion string of the probabilities for the various types. The probability for each string of types is the product of the elements in the companion probability string. Also, for each type a matrix of the frequency of that type in each string is developed.

_____ MATLAB Script _____

```
% file multinom.m
% Multinomial distribution (small N, m)
% Version of 10/27/93
N = input('Enter the number of trials  ');
m = input('Enter the number of types   ');
p = input('Enter the type probabilities  ');
M = 1:m;
T = zeros(m^N,N);
for i = 1:N
  a = ones(m^(i-1),1)*M;
  a = a(:);
  a = a*ones(1,m^(N-i));
  T(:,N-i+1) = a(:);      % All possible strings of the types
end
MT = zeros(m^N,m);
for i = 1:m
  MT(:,i) = sum(T'==i)';
end
clear T                   % To conserve memory
disp('String frequencies for type k are in column matrix MT(:,k)')
P = zeros(m^N,N);
for i = 1:N
  a = ones(m^(i-1),1)*p;
  a = a(:);
  a = a*ones(1,m^(N-i));
  P(:,N-i+1) = a(:);      % Strings of type probabilities
end
PS = prod(P');            % Probability of each string
clear P                   % To conserve memory
disp('String probabilities are in row matrix PS')
```

EXAMPLE 3.8
Continuation of
the Candy Problem

Suppose six pieces are selected. What is the probability of getting at least 2 red (first type) and at least one yellow (third type)?

———————————————— MATLAB Script ————————————————

```
>> multinom
Enter the number of trials  6
Enter the number of types   4
Enter the type probabilities  [0.23 0.30 0.25 0.22]
String frequencies for type k are in column matrix MT(:,k)
Individual string probabilities are in row matrix PS
>> Q = (MT(:,1) >= 2)&(MT(:,3) >= 1);   % A column matrix— ones for those
% strings satisfying the conditions
>> PQ = PS*Q
PQ  =  0.3123
```

——●

A simple argument based on generating functions shows that the sum of independent binomial random variables with the same parameter p is binomial. Although the N_k do not form an independent class, the structure of the problem ensures that the sum of one or more of the N_k has a binomial distribution with probability of success which is the sum of the probabilities for the types combined. Suppose, for example, the outcome of a trial is represented by a card with a number designating the type. Also, suppose that cards with type numbers 1, 3, and 4 are all red cards. We can create a "supertype" red. Now type red occurs iff one of the types 1, 3, or 4 occurs. The probability of type red on any trial is thus $p_1 + p_3 + p_4$. If $R_i =$ the event of a red type on the ith trial, the independence of types for different trials ensures the class $\{R_i: 1 \leq i \leq N\}$ satisfies the Bernoulli trial conditions, with $P(R_i) = p_1 + p_3 + p_4$. This means that $N_R = N_1 + N_3 + N_4 \sim$ binomial $(N, p_1 + p_3 + p_4)$. This pattern generalizes in obvious ways. A formal verification is made easily by examining the expressions for the N_k in terms of the indicator functions. Consider the case of the sum of two

$$N_k + N_J = \sum_{i=1}^{N} I_{E_{ki}} + \sum_{i=1}^{N} I_{E_{ji}} = \sum_{i=1}^{N} (I_{E_{ki}} + I_{E_{ji}}) = \sum_{i=1}^{N} I_{E_i}$$

Because the pair $\{E_{ki}, E_{ji}\}$ is mutually exclusive, $E_i = E_{ki} \uplus E_{ji}$ and $P(E_i) = p_k + p_j$. Under the independence assumptions, the class $\{E_i: 1 \leq i \leq N\}$ is independent, with probability p invariant with i. It is apparent that the same pattern holds for any subset of types.

EXAMPLE 3.9
The Candy Problem Again

Suppose Mary is interested only in the red and green candies. She selects at random twenty pieces. What is the probability she gets ten or more of the kinds she prefers?

Solution

We have a new type: red or green. An outcome of this type occurs iff the outcome is of Type 1 or Type 2. The probability of this type on any trial is $p_1 + p_2 = 0.23 + 0.30 = 0.53$. $N_{RG} \sim$ binomial $(20, 0.53)$. Hence,

$$P(N_{RG} \geq 8) = \text{cbinom}(20, 0.53, 10) = 0.6896$$

5. SUMMARY DATA ON SOME COMMON DISTRIBUTIONS

DISCRETE DISTRIBUTIONS

1. **Indicator functions** $X = I_E$ $\quad P(X = 1) = P(E) = p$
   $P(X = 0) = q = 1 - p$

   $E[X] = p \quad \text{Var}[X] = pq \quad M_X(s) = q + pe^s \quad g_X(s) = q + ps$

2. **Simple random variable** $X = \sum_{i=1}^{n} t_i I_{A_i}$ (canonical form)
   $P(X = t_i) = P(A_i) = p_i$

   $$E[X] = \sum_{i=1}^{n} t_i p_i \quad \text{Var}[X] = \sum_{i=1}^{n} t_i^2 p_i q_i - 2 \sum_{i<j} t_i t_j p_i p_j$$

   $$M_X(s) = \sum_{i=1}^{n} p_i e^{st_i}$$

3. **Binomial** (n, p) $\quad X = \sum_{i=1}^{n} I_{E_i}$ with $\{I_{E_i}: 1 \leq i \leq n\}$ iid $P(E_i) = p$

   $E[X] = np \quad \text{Var}[X] = npq \quad M_X(s) = (q + pe^s)^n$
   $g_X(s) = (q + ps)^n$

   MATLAB: $P(X = k) = \text{ibinom}(n, p, k)$
   $P(X \geq k) = \text{cbinom}(n, p, k)$

4. **Geometric** (p) $\quad P(X = k) = pq^k \quad \forall\, k \geq 0$

   $$E[X] = q/p \quad \text{Var}[X] = q/p^2 \quad M_X(s) = \frac{p}{1 - qe^s}$$

   $$g_X(s) = \frac{p}{1 - qs}$$

   If $Y - 1 \sim$ geometric (p), so that $P(Y = k) = pq^{k-1} \; \forall\, k \geq 1$, then

   $$E[Y] = 1/p \quad \text{Var}[X] = q/p^2 \quad M_Y(s) = \frac{pe^s}{1 - qe^s}$$

$$g_Y(s) = \frac{ps}{1 - qs}$$

5. **Negative binomial** (m, p) $P(X = k) =$
$C(m + k - 1, m - 1)p^m q^k$ $\forall\, k \geq 0$, where X is equal to
the number of failures before the mth success.

$$E[X] = mq/p \qquad \mathrm{Var}[X] = mq/p^2 \qquad M_X(s) = \left[\frac{p}{1 - qe^s}\right]^m$$

$$g_X(s) = \left[\frac{p}{1 - qs}\right]^m$$

For $Y_m = X_m + m$, the number of the trial on which the mth success
occurs. $P(Y = k) = C(k - 1,\ m - 1)p^m q^{k-m}\ \forall\, k \geq m$.

$$E[Y] = m/p \qquad \mathrm{Var}[Y] = mq/p^2 \qquad M_Y(s) = \left(\frac{pe^s}{1 - qe^s}\right)^m$$

$$g_Y(s) = \left(\frac{ps}{1 - qs}\right)^m$$

MATLAB: $P(Y = k) = $ nbinom (m, p, k)

6. **Poisson** (μ) $P(X = k) = e^{-\mu}\frac{\mu^k}{k!}\ \forall\, k \geq 0$

$$E[X] = \mu \qquad \mathrm{Var}[X] = \mu \qquad M_X(s) = e^{\mu(e^s - 1)} \qquad g_X(s) = e^{\mu(s - 1)}$$

MATLAB: $P(X = k) = $ ipoisson(m, k) $P(X \geq k) = $ cpoisson(m, k)

ABSOLUTELY CONTINUOUS DISTRIBUTIONS

1. **Uniform** (a, b) $f_X(t) = \frac{1}{b-a}\ a < t < b$ (zero elsewhere)

$$E[X] = \frac{b + a}{2} \qquad \mathrm{Var}[X] = \frac{(b - a)^2}{12} \qquad M_X(s) = \frac{e^{sb} - e^{sa}}{s(b - a)}$$

2. **Symmetric triangular** $(-a, a)$ $f_X(t) = \begin{cases} (a + t)/a^2 & -a \leq t < 0 \\ (a - t)/a^2 & 0 \leq t \leq a \end{cases}$

$$E[X] = 0 \qquad \mathrm{Var}[X] = \frac{a^2}{6}$$

$$M_X(s) = \frac{e^{as} + e^{-as} - 2}{a^2 s^2} = \frac{e^{as} - 1}{as} \cdot \frac{1 - e^{-as}}{as}$$

3. **Exponential** (λ) $f_X(t) = \lambda e^{-\lambda t}\ t \geq 0$

$$E[X] = \frac{1}{\lambda} \qquad \mathrm{Var}[X] = \frac{1}{\lambda^2} \qquad M_X(s) = \frac{\lambda}{\lambda - s}$$

4. **Gamma** (α, λ) $f_X(t) = \frac{\lambda^\alpha t^{\alpha-1} e^{-\lambda t}}{\Gamma(\alpha)}\ t \geq 0$

$$E[X] = \frac{\alpha}{\lambda} \qquad \mathrm{Var}[X] = \frac{\alpha}{\lambda^2} \qquad M_X(s) = \left(\frac{\lambda}{\lambda - s}\right)^\alpha$$

MATLAB: $P(X \leq t) = $ gammadbn (α, λ, t)

5. **Normal** $N(\mu, \sigma^2)$ $f_X(t) = \frac{1}{\sigma\sqrt{2\pi}} \exp\left(-\frac{1}{2}\left(\frac{t-\mu}{\sigma}\right)^2\right)$

$$E[X] = \mu \qquad \text{Var}[X]\sigma^2 \qquad M_X(s) = \exp\left(\frac{\sigma^2 s^2}{2} + \mu s\right)$$

MATLAB: $P(X \le t) = \text{gaussian}(\mu, \sigma^2, t)$

6. **Beta** (r, s)

$$f_X(t) = \frac{\Gamma(r)\Gamma(s)}{\Gamma(r+s)} t^{r-1}(1-t)^{s-1} \qquad 0 < t < 1, \ r > 0, \ s > 0$$

$$E[X] = \frac{r}{r+s} \qquad \text{Var}[X] = \frac{rs}{(r+s)^2(r+s+1)}$$

MATLAB: $f_X(t) = \text{beta}(r, s, t)$ $P(X \le t) = \text{betadbn}(r, s, t)$

7. **Weibull** (alpha, lambda, nu)

$$F_X(t) = 1 - e^{\lambda(t-\nu)^\alpha}, \qquad \alpha > 0, \ \lambda > 0, \ \nu \ge 0, \ t \ge \nu$$

$$E[X] = \frac{1}{\lambda^{1/\alpha}} \Gamma(1 + 1/\alpha) + \nu$$

$$\text{Var}[X] = \frac{1}{\lambda^{2/\alpha}} \left[\Gamma(1 + 2/\lambda) - \Gamma^2(1 + 1/\lambda)\right]$$

MATLAB: ($\nu = 0$ only)

$$f_X(t) = \text{weibull}(alpha, lambda, t)$$
$$P(X \le t) = \text{weibulld}(alpha, lambda, t)$$

POISSON APPROXIMATION TO THE BINOMIAL DISTRIBUTION

If $X \sim$ binomial (n, p), with n large and p small enough to keep the product np moderate, then X is approximately Poisson (np). That is,

$$P(X = n) = C(n, k) p^k (1-p)^{n-k} \approx e^{np} \frac{(np)^k}{k!}$$

RELATIONSHIP BETWEEN GAMMA AND POISSON DISTRIBUTIONS

1. If $X \sim$ gamma (n, λ), then $P(X \le t) = P(Y \ge n)$ where $Y \sim$ Poisson (λt).
2. If $Y \sim$ Poisson (λt), then $P(Y \ge n) = P(X \le t)$ where $X \sim$ gamma (n, λ).

SUMMARY DATA ON SOME COMMON DISTRIBUTIONS

REINFORCEMENT EXERCISES AND EXPLORATION PROBLEMS

■

REINFORCEMENT EXERCISES

The following problems are suggestive. Most textbooks will have many such problems.

P3.1 In a Bernoulli sequence with probability 0.2 of success on any trial:

    a. What is the probability of three or more successes in the first 10 trials?

    b. Determine the probability that the third success will occur no sooner than the fifth and no later than the tenth trial.

P3.2 Random variable X is Poisson (2.5). Use cumulative probabilities to determine $P(X = 3)$ and $P(2 \leq X \leq 5)$.

P3.3 The number of calls to a switchboard in an hour is Poisson (10). What is the probability of no more than four calls?

P3.4 The number of voltage surges on a power line in an hour is a random quantity $X \sim$ Poisson (7). Determine $P(4 \leq X \leq 9)$.

P3.5 For $X \sim$ gamma $(2, 1/2)$, determine $P(X \geq 2)$.

P3.6 For $X \sim$ beta $(3, 2)$, determine $P(0.21 < X \leq 0.57)$.

P3.7 Random variable $X \sim N(9, 17)$. Determine $P(7 \leq X \leq 9.5)$ and $P(|X - 9| \geq 1.7)$.

P3.8 For $X \sim N(\mu, \sigma^2)$, determine $P(|X - \mu| < a\sigma)$ for $a = 0.25, 0.50, 0.75, 1, 2,$ and 3.

P3.9 The result of extensive quality control sampling shows that digital watches coming off a production line have accuracy, in seconds per month, that is normally distributed with $\mu = 5$, $\sigma^2 = 300$. The watches are tested individually and graded. To achieve top grade, a watch must have an accuracy in the range of -5 to $+10$ seconds per month. What is the probability that a watch taken from the production line will achieve top grade?

P3.10 If $X \sim N(3, 16)$, determine $P(X^2 - 3X + 2 < 0)$ and $P(\log(X + 1) > 0)$.

P3.11 Fifty students take an examination. The time to completion (in minutes) for the ith student is a random quantity X_i. If these form an iid class, with each X_i exponential and having expected value 45, what is the probability that ten or more will not have completed the test in one hour?

P3.12 The sum of ten iid random variables, each exponential ($\lambda = 0.25$), is a random variable $S \sim$ gamma $(10, 0.25)$. *Use the Poisson distribution* to determine $P(S \leq 40)$.

P3.13 Suppose the class $\{X, Y, Z\}$ is independent, with $X \sim$ gamma $(3, 0.3)$, $Y \sim$ gamma $(1.2, 0.1)$, and $Z \sim$ exponential (0.12). Let $V := \min\{X, Y, Z\}$. Determine $P(V \geq 2)$.

P3.14 Five solid state modules are installed in a computer system. If the modules are not defective, they have practically unlimited life. However, with probability $p = 0.05$, any unit could have a defect that results in a lifetime, in hours, which is exponential (0.0025).

    a. What is the probability that no module fails in the first 500 hours?

    b. Suppose the system operates if four or more modules are operative. What is the probability the system operates for at least 500 hours?

Note. For an alternate solution to part (a), see the solution to Reinforcement Problem P7.21.

EXPLORATION PROBLEMS

P3.1 Approximation of the Binomial by the Poisson and Gaussian Distributions. For various values of n and p, calculate individual binomial and Poisson terms, then sum them using the MATLAB function *cumsum*, to form the distribution function at the integer values. Pick out a range of values of t around the mean value np sufficient to give a good representation for the binomial distribution function. For example, for $n = 1000$ and $p = 0.01$, a good range is $k = 0:20$. This strategy may be implemented by the following procedure. Given the values of n and p, it picks out a range of about two standard deviations, then calculates and plots the cumulative distribution functions.

––––––––––––––––––––––– MATLAB Script –––––––––––––––––––––––

```
% file bincomp.m
% Comparison of binomial, Poisson, and Gaussian
% Version of 10/25/93
n = input('Enter the parameter n  ');
p = input('Enter the parameter p  ');
k = floor(n*p-2*sqrt(n*p)):floor(n*p+2*sqrt(n*p));
Fb = cumsum(ibinom(n,p,0:n));      % Binomial distribution function
Fp = cumsum(ipoisson(n*p,0:n));    % Poisson distribution function
Fg = gaussian(n*p,n*p*(1 - p),k);  % Gaussian distribution function
plot(k,Fb(k+1))                    % Plotting detals
hold on
plot(k,Fp(k+1),'o')
plot(k,Fg,'+')
hold off
xlabel('t values')                 % Graph labeling details
ylabel('Distribution function')
title('Binomial (solid)  Poisson (o o o)  Gaussian (+ + +)')
grid
```

Continues

```
disp('Binomial— solid')
disp('Poisson—  o o o')
disp('Gaussian— + + +')
```

Calculate for $p = 0.1$ and again for $p = 0.6$. How do you account for the difference in approximations to the binomial in the various cases? The mean values are the same for the three distributions in each of the three cases. What about the variances? Why should the gaussian approximation appear to change? Try other values of n and p to check your explanations.

Note: that this exploration is possible because the function *ibinomial* has high precision for large values of n (see comments on precision in the discussion of the binomial distribution) and *ipoisson* is good for $\mu = np$ up to about 700.

P3.2 Approximating the Poisson by the Gaussian Distribution. We should expect a better approximation of the Poisson by the gaussian if the means and variances match. The following procedure makes such calculations and plots the result, given any value of the parameter μ up to about 700.

—————————————————— MATLAB Script ——————————————————

```
% file poissapp.m
% Comparison of Poisson and gaussian distributions
% Version of 2/23/94
mu = input('Enter the parameter mu  ');
n = floor(1.5*mu);
k = floor(mu-2*sqrt(mu)):floor(mu+2*sqrt(mu));
FP = cumsum(ipoisson(mu,0:n));
FG = gaussian(mu,mu,k);
plot(k,FP(k))
hold on
plot(k,FG,'o')
hold off
grid
xlabel('t values')
ylabel('Distribution function')
title('Poisson— solid line;  Gaussian— o o o')
disp('Poisson—  solid')
disp('Gaussian— o o o')
```

Try various values of μ. Does the precision of approximation change appreciably? Is there some theoretical basis for this?

P3.3 Approximating a Density with the Beta Distribution. Consider the density function

$$f_X(t) = \pi t \, \sin(\pi t), \qquad 0 \le t \le 1$$

Plot this function against t, then determine experimentally the parameters r, s

to get a reasonable approximation to a "best fit" with the beta (r, s) distribution. Use information on the maximum of the density and the variance as functions of r, s to guide experimentation. Try approximating other densities on $[0, 1]$.

P3.4 Some Analysis of Multinomial Trials. Suppose there are N trials (sometimes called arrivals), each of which results in one of m types. Let E_{ki} = the event the ith trial gives a result of the kth type. The random variable whose value is the type of the ith result may be expressed

$$T_i = \sum_{k=1}^{m} k I_{E_{ki}} \qquad 1 \le i \le N$$

Note that for each i, the class $\{E_{ki}: 1 \le k \le m\}$ is a partition, since on each trial the outcome is of one, and only one, type. We assume that successive outcomes are independent and the probabilities of each type remain invariant with i. Specifically, we assume

a. $\{T_i: 1 \le i \le N\}$ is an independent class.
b. $P(E_{ki}) = p_k \ 1 \le k \le m$, invariant with i.

If N_k is the number of outcomes of type k, then

$$N_k = \sum_{i=1}^{N} I_{E_{ki}} \quad \text{which is binomial} \ (N, p_k) \qquad 1 \le k \le m$$

If B_r is the number of types for which there are exactly r results in N trials and if D_r is the number of types for which there are r or more results in N trials, then

$$B_r = \sum_{k=1}^{m} I_{\{N_k=r\}} \quad \text{and} \quad D_r = \sum_{k=1}^{m} I_{\{N_k \ge r\}}$$

Since $N_1 + N_2 + \cdots + N_m = N$, the N_k do not form an independent class, nor are they mutually exclusive. Thus, obtaining distributions for B_r and D_r may be quite difficult, except in very special cases. However, because of linearity the expectations are simply

$$E[B_r] = \sum_{k=1}^{m} P(N_k = r) \quad \text{and} \quad E[D_r] = \sum_{k=1}^{m} P(N_k \ge r)$$

The following are exercises using these patterns.

a. An airport bus deposits 25 passengers at seven stops. Assume that each passenger is as likely to get off at any stop as another and that they act independently. The bus stops only if someone wants to get off.
   i. What is the expected number of stops that it makes?
   ii. What is the expected number of stops at which three or more passengers depart? *Suggestion:* Model as $N = 25$ trials, with $m = 7$ types of outcomes.

b. One thousand persons are chosen at random. Suppose birthdays are independent and each one is equally likely to have any of the 365 days of the year (ignore leap years).

    i. What is the probability that five or more persons will have July 4 as their birthday?

    ii. What is the expected number of birthdays on July 4?

    iii. What is the expected number of days in the year on which there are five or more birthdays?

c. A computer store has a sale offering special prices on the first 100 personal computers sold. Five types of computers are included in the sale: (1) Macintosh Classic, (2) Macintosh LCIII, (3) Compaq 386, (4) Dell 386, and (5) IBM PS/2. The respective probabilities for each type on a sale are 0.1, 0.2, 0.3, 0.2, and 0.2.

What is the probability of selling at least 30 Macintoshes (of either type)? What is the expected number of computer types for which sales are 20 or more?

d. K. L. Chung: *Elementary Probability Theory with Stochastic Processes* points out that the following *occupancy problem* may be interpreted in terms of this model. Put N tokens in m boxes, with each token equally likely to go into any of the m boxes. Express the occupancy problem as a sequence of multinomial trials, and formulate the appropriate questions.

P3.5 Order Statistics. Suppose $\{X_i: 1 \le i \le n\}$ is iid, with common distribution function F. Let $Y_1 =$ the smallest of the X_i, $Y_2 =$ the next larger, $\cdots$, $Y_n =$ the largest. Then Y_k is called the kth *order statistic* for the class $\{X_i: 1 \le i \le n\}$. We wish to determine the distribution functions

$$F_k(t) = P(Y_k \le t) \qquad 1 \le k \le n$$

Now $Y_k \le t$ iff k or more of the X_i have values no greater than t. We may analyze the system as a Bernoulli sequence of n trials, with a success on the ith trial iff $X_i \le t$. The probability of success on any trial is $p = P(X \le t) = F(t)$. Hence,

$$F_k(t) = \sum_{j=k}^{n} C(n, j) F^j(t)[1 - F(t)]^{n-j}$$

Thus, $F_k(t)$ is obtained as a value of the cumulative binomial distribution with $p = F(t)$ and n the size of the sample. Ordinarily, the values of n and p will not correspond to any table entry. However, the freedom of the function cbinom with respect to the choice of n and p allows easy determination.

ILLUSTRATIVE EXERCISE

Suppose a sample of size $n = 100$ is taken from a normal population with mean 11 and variance 30. That is, the X_i are iid, $N(11, 30)$. What is the value of $F_{70}(13)$, the probability the 70th order statistic is no greater than 13?

RANDOM VARIABLES AND DISTRIBUTIONS

Simple Random Variables

PREVIEW

Simple random variables take on only a finite set of values. They may be represented in useful ways with the aid of indicator functions introduced in Section 1.4, the appendix to Chapter 1.

Perhaps the most common form of representation of a simple random variable X is as an affine combination (linear combination plus a constant) of indicator functions.

$$X = a_0 + a_1 I_{E_1} + a_2 I_{E_2} + \cdots + a_m I_{E_m}$$

This *affine* form is the most natural way to represent a simple random variable in many modeling situations.

An alternate form, which we call *canonical* (or standard) form, exhibits the various possible values taken on by the random variable. If $\{t_1, t_2, \cdots, t_n\}$ is the set of distinct values and $A_i = \{X = t_i\}$ is the event the value t_i is taken on, then

$$X = t_1 I_{A_1} + t_2 I_{A_2} + \cdots + t_n I_{A_n}$$

The *distribution* for X consists of the set of values $\{t_1, t_2, \cdots, t_n\}$ and the corresponding probabilities $\{p_1, p_2, \cdots, p_n\}$, where $p_i = P(X = t_i)$.

The affine form shows that X is constant on each of the minterms generated by $\{E_1, E_2, \cdots, E_m\}$. This fact is used to convert from affine form to canonical form. An intermediate *primitive* form is obtained by determining the value of X on each minterm. Thus, if the minterms are $\{M_0, M_1, \cdots, M_q\}$, we have

$$X = s_0 I_{M_0} + s_1 I_{M_1} + \cdots + s_q I_{M_q}$$

Conversion from affine form to canonical form is achieved by sorting the values for the primitive form and adding the probabilities associated with each distinct value.

Once the distribution for X is determined, a variety of quantities related to the random variable may be determined. These include the probability that X takes on one of a specified set of values as well as the expectation $E[X]$ and variance Var$[X]$. Also, simple techniques are developed to determine the distribution of the variable $Z = g(X)$ for any reasonable functions g defined on the range of X.

1. REPRESENTATIONS USING INDICATOR FUNCTIONS

Simple random variables, which take on only a finite number of values, play a pivotal role in probability theory. In part, this stems from the fact that any bounded, real random variable may be approximated uniformly as closely as desired by simple random variables. Concepts such as mathematical expectation and conditional expectation find their simplest and most transparent formulations in the case of simple random variables. We begin with an analysis of a single real-valued, simple random variable.

In order to deal with simple random variables clearly and precisely, we must find suitable ways to express them analytically. We do this with the aid of *indicator functions* introduced in the appendix to Chapter 1. Two basic forms and an auxiliary intermediate form are encountered.

CANONICAL FORM

Standard or *canonical form* displays the possible values and the corresponding events. If X takes on distinct values $\{t_1, t_2, \cdots, t_n\}$ with corresponding probabilities $\{p_1, p_2, \cdots, p_n\}$ and $A_i = \{X = t_i\}$, $1 \le i \le n$, then $\{A_1, A_2, \cdots, A_n\}$ is a partition (i.e., on any trial, exactly one of these events occurs). We may write

$$X = t_1 I_{A_1} + t_2 I_{A_2} + \cdots + t_n I_{A_n} = \sum_{i=1}^{n} t_i I_{A_i}$$

If $X(\omega) = t_i$, then $\omega \in A_i$, so that $I_{A_i}(\omega) = 1$ and all the other indicator functions in the sum have value zero. The summation expression thus picks out the correct value t_i. This is true for any t_i, so the expression represents $X(\omega)$ for all ω.

Note that in canonical form, if one of the t_i has value zero, we include that term. For some probability distributions it may be that $P(A_i) = 0$ for one or more of the t_i. In that case, we call these values *null values,* for they can only occur with probability zero and hence are practically impossible. In the general formulation, we include possible null values, since they do not affect any probability calculations.

AFFINE FORM

We commonly have X represented in *affine form* in which the random variable is represented as an affine combination of indicator functions

$$X = a_0 + a_1 I_{E_1} + a_2 I_{E_2} + \cdots + a_m I_{E_m} = a_0 + \sum_{j=1}^{m} a_j I_{E_j}$$

In this form, the class $\{E_1, E_2, \cdots, E_m\}$ is not necessarily mutually exclusive, and the coefficients do not display directly the set of possible values. In fact, the E_i often form an independent class.

●────────

EXAMPLE 4.1
Binomial Counting
Random Variable

Consider the random variable S_n which counts the number of successes in a sequence of n Bernoulli trials. If E_i is the event of a success on the ith trial, then one natural way to express the count is

$$S_n = \sum_{i=1}^{n} I_{E_i}, \quad \text{with } P(E_i) = p \quad 1 \le i \le n$$

This is affine form with $a_0 = 0$ and $a_i = 1$ for $1 \le i \le n$. In this case, the E_i cannot form a mutually exclusive class, since they form an independent class. As the analysis of Bernoulli trials and the binomial distribution shows, canonical form must be

$$S_n = \sum_{k=0}^{n} k\, I_{A_k} \quad \text{with } P(A_k) = C(n,k) p^k (1-p)^{n-k} \quad 0 \le k \le n$$

────────●

For both theoretical and practical purposes, canonical form is desirable. For one thing, it displays directly the range (i.e., set of values) of the random variable. The distribution consists of the values $\{t_k : 1 \le k \le n\}$ paired with the corresponding probabilities $\{p_k : 1 \le k \le n\}$, where $p_k = P(A_k) = P(X = t_k)$.

FINDING THE DISTRIBUTION FROM AFFINE FORM

If we have X in affine form, we have a *systematic procedure for finding canonical form*. To develop this, we utilize appropriate facts about indicator functions and minterms generated by a finite class of events.

1. In the treatment of the minterm expansion, we note that each indicator function I_{E_i} is constant on each minterm generated by the

class $\{E_1, E_2, \cdots, E_m\}$, so that X is constant on each minterm. We determine the value s_i of X on each minterm M_i. This describes X in primitive form.

2. In many cases, some values of X may be achieved on more than one minterm. Suppose, for example, $X = 3$ on minterms M_2, M_5, M_9. Then the event $\{X = 3\} = M_2 \uplus M_5 \uplus M_9$, so that

$$P(X = 3) = P(M_2) + P(M_5) + P(M_9)$$

3. In order to obtain the distribution, the values must first be sorted and then the minterm probabilities for equal values must be added.

We illustrate with a simple example. Extension to the general case should be quite evident. First, we do the problem in tabular form. Then we consider MATLAB procedures to carry out the desired operations.

EXAMPLE 4.2
Finding the Distribution from Affine Form

A mail-order house is featuring three items (limit one each per customer). Let

E_1 = the event the customer orders Item 1 for 10 dollars

E_2 = the event the customer orders Item 2 for 18 dollars

E_3 = the event the customer orders Item 3 for 10 dollars

We suppose $\{E_1, E_2, E_3\}$ is independent with probabilities 0.6, 0.3, and 0.5, respectively. Note that a customer may place an order for other items in the store but order none of the special items. Let X be the amount a customer spends on the special items. Then, in affine form,

$$X = 10I_{E_1} + 18I_{E_2} + 10I_{E_3}$$

We seek first the primitive form, using the minterm probabilities (actually calculated using minprob).

i	$10I_{E_i}$	$18I_{E_i}$	$10I_{Ei}$	s_i	pm_i
0	0	0	0	0	0.14
1	0	0	10	10	0.14
2	0	18	0	18	0.06
3	0	18	10	28	0.06
4	10	0	0	10	0.21
5	10	0	10	20	0.21
6	10	18	0	28	0.09
7	10	18	10	38	0.09

We then sort the values s_i on the various M_i to expose more clearly the primitive form for X.

i	s_i	pm_i
0	0	0.14
1	10	0.14
4	10	0.21
2	18	0.06
5	20	0.21
3	28	0.06
6	28	0.09
7	38	0.09

The primitive form of X is thus

$$X = 0I_{M_0} + 10I_{M_1} + 10I_{M_4} + 18I_{M_2} + 20I_{M_5} + 28I_{M_3}$$
$$+ 28I_{M_6} + 38I_{M_7}$$

To get the distribution, we list the distinct values and add together the probabilities of the minterms on which each value is taken. This gives us a matrix X of possible values and a corresponding matrix PX of probabilities that X takes on each of these values. Examination of the table shows that

$$X = [0\ 10\ 18\ 20\ 28\ 38] \quad \text{and} \quad PX = [0.14\ \ 0.35\ \ 0.06\ \ 0.21\ \ 0.15\ \ 0.09]$$

2. MATLAB IMPLEMENTATION

We now consider MATLAB procedures for carrying out the transformation. We start with the random variable in affine form and suppose we have available, or can calculate, the minterm probabilities. We may use the following procedure to determine the primitive form.

————————————————— MATLAB Script —————————————————

```
%  file prim.m
% Version of 7/19/93
% To determine the distribution for a simple random variable
%   in affine form, when the minterm probabilities are available.
% Assumes the program mintable is available
disp('Coefficient vector must contain the constant term')
disp('If the constant term is zero, enter 0 in the last place')
c = input(' Enter row vector of coefficients ');
pm = input(' Enter row vector of minterm probabilities ');
n = length(c) - 1;
if 2^n ~= length(pm)
   error('Incorrect minterm probability vector length');
end
```

Continues

```
M = mintable(n);              % Provides a table of minterm patterns
C = ones(2^n,1)*c(1:n);       % 2^n rows of coefficients of indicators
a = C'.*M;                    % Multiplies coefficients into mintable
s = sum(a) + c(n+1);          % Adds constant to column sums of matrix a
[Y,I] = sort(s);
D = [0:(2^n -1); s; pm];
X = D(:,I)';
if pm == 0
  h = ['    i     si'];
else
  h = ['      i        si         pmi'];
end
disp(' ')
disp('Minterm values and probabilities')
disp('      sorted by values si')
disp(h)
disp(X)
```

●━━━━━━━━━━

EXAMPLE 4.3
Continuation of
Example 4.2

───────────────────── MATLAB Script ─────────────────────

```
>> pm = minprob([0.6 0.3 0.5]);
>> c = [10 18 10 0];
>> prim
Coefficient vector must contain the constant term
If the constant term is zero, enter 0 in the last place
 Enter row vector of coefficients c
 Enter row vector of minterm probabilities pm
Minterm values and probabilities
      sorted by values si
      i        si        pmi
      0         0       0.1400
 1.0000   10.0000      0.1400
 4.0000   10.0000      0.2100
 2.0000   18.0000      0.0600
 5.0000   20.0000      0.2100
 3.0000   28.0000      0.0600
 6.0000   28.0000      0.0900
 7.0000   38.0000      0.0900
```

━━━━━━━━━━●

While this result displays the values on each minterm, it is desirable that
the program determine the actual distribution for X and make it available in the
MATLAB workspace for further calculations. This end is achieved by using

the procedure csort on the pair (s, pm), where s is the matrix of values on the minterms and pm is the matrix of corresponding minterm probabilities. The following procedure is the same as the procedure primitive up to the point of sorting. At this point, the user defined function csort is employed.

_____ MATLAB Script _____

```
% file canonic.m
% To determine the distribution for a simple random variable
%  in affine form, when the minterm probabilities are available.
% Assumes the programs mintable and csort are available
% version of 4/16/94
disp('Coefficient vector must contain the constant term')
disp('If the constant term is zero, enter 0 in the last place')
c = input(' Enter row vector of coefficients  ');
pm = input(' Enter row vector of minterm probabilities  ');
n = length(c) - 1;
if 2^n ~= length(pm)
   error('Incorrect minterm probability vector length');
end
M = mintable(n);            % Provides a table of minterm patterns
C = ones(2^n,1)*c(1:n);    % 2^n rows of coefficients of indicators
a = C'.*M;                  % Multiplies coefficients into mintable
s = sum(a) + c(n+1);       % Adds constant to  column sums of matrix a
d = csort(s,pm);           % Details for values and probabilities
X = d(1,:);
PX = d(2,:);
XDBN = d';
disp('Use row matrices X and PX for calculations')
disp('Call for XDBN to view the distribution')
```

EXAMPLE 4.4
Continuation of
Example 4.3
_____ MATLAB Script _____

```
>>c = [10 18 10 0];
>>pm = minprob(0.1*[6 3 5]);
>>canonic
Coefficient vector must contain the constant term
If the constant term is zero, enter 0 in the last place
Enter row vector of coefficients   c
Enter row vector of minterm probabilities   pm
Use row matrices X and PX for calculations
Call for XDBN to view the distribution
>>disp(XDBN)            % Optional display
```

Continues

```
        0      0.1400
  10.0000      0.3500
  18.0000      0.0600
  20.0000      0.2100
  28.0000      0.1500
  38.0000      0.0900
```

3. PROBABILITIES, EXPECTATIONS, AND FUNCTIONS OF A RANDOM VARIABLE

■

KEY STRATEGIES

With the distribution available in the row matrices X (set of values) and PX (set of probabilities), we may calculate a wide variety of quantities associated with the random variable X. There are two key strategies:

1. Use relational and logical operations on the matrix of values X to determine a zero-one matrix M which has ones in those positions corresponding to values which meet a prescribed condition. Then, to determine $P(X \in M)$, we give the MATLAB command

$$PM = M^*PX'$$

This has the effect of picking out the appropriate minterm probabilities and adding them.

2. Determine $G = g(X) = [g(t_1)g(t_2) \cdots g(t_n)]$ by using array operations on matrix X. A procedure which we call *gdbn* is used to apply csort to the pair (G, PX) to get the distribution for $Z = g(X)$. This distribution may be used to determine the expectation of $g(X)$ and probabilities that $g(X)$ satisfies various conditions.

———————————— MATLAB Script ————————————

```
%  file gdbn.m
% Determines distribution for Z = g(X)
% Version of 4/16/94
% Assumes X = matrix of X values
%          PX = matrix of P(X=t)
%          G = matrix of g(X)
%          Procedure csort
GDBN = csort(G,PX)';
Z =   GDBN(:,1)';
PZ = GDBN(:,2)';
disp('Z is a row matrix of Z = g(X) values')
disp('PZ is a row matrix of P(Z=z)')
disp('To view the distribution for Z = g(X), call for GDBN')
```

SIMPLE RANDOM VARIABLES

MATLAB OPERATIONS

We illustrate with some examples. At first, we utilize the example above. The procedure canonic has given us the distribution for X in the matrices X and PX.

1. $P(\{X \leq 15\} \uplus \{X > 25\})$.

———————————— MATLAB Script ————————————
```
>>M = (X <= 15)|(X > 25);   % Matrix with ones where condition is met
>>PM = M*PX'                 % Picks out and sums those probabilities
PM = 0.7300
```

2. $E[X] = \sum_{i=1}^{n} t_i P(X = t_i)$

———————————— MATLAB Script ————————————
```
>>EX = X*PX'
EX = 16.4000
```

3. $\text{Var}\,[X] = E[X^2] - E[X]^2$

———————————— MATLAB Script ————————————
```
>>EX2 = (X.^2)*PX'
EX2 =   386
>>VX = EX2 - EX^2
VX = 117.0400
```

4. $Z = g(X) = X^{1/2} - X + 50$

———————————— MATLAB Script ————————————
```
>>G = sqrt(X) - X + 50;
>>gdbn
Z is a row matrix of Z = g(X) values
PZ is a row matrix of P(Z=v)
To view the distribution for Z = g(X), call for GDBN
>>disp(GDBN)
   18.1644      0.0900
   27.2915      0.1500
   34.4721      0.2100
   36.2426      0.0600
   43.1623      0.3500
   50.0000      0.1400
```

5. $P(20 < Z \le 40)$, where $Z = g(X) = X^{1/2} - X + 50$

We make two equivalent approaches. First, we determine the values of X for which $g(X)$ satisfies the inequalities and add the probabilities that X takes those values. Next, we determine the values of Z for which the inequalities are satisfied and add the probabilities that Z takes those values.

_____ MATLAB Script _____

```
>>M = (20 < G)&(G <= 40)    % Matrix M has ones where g(X) satisfies the
                               inequalities
M = 0      0    1    1    1    0
>>PXM = M*PX'
PXM = 0.4200                % Probability X takes on those values
>>
>>N = (20 < v)&(v <= 40)    % Matrix N has ones where Z satisfies the
                               inequalities
N = 0      1    1    1    0    0
>>PZN = N*PZ'
PZN = 0.4200                % Probability Z takes on those values
```

When we have the distribution for X, whether obtained from canonic or otherwise, we have a program *simple* which names the matrix of values t and the matrix of probabilities PX and then calculates $E[X]$, $E[X^2]$, and $\mathrm{Var}[X]$.

_____ MATLAB Script _____

```
% file simple.m
% Calculates basic quantities for simple random variables
% Version of 4/16/94
X =   input('Enter row matrix of X-values   ');
PX =  input('Enter row matrix PX of X probabilities   ');
n = length(X);         % dimension of X
EX = X*PX'             % E[X]
EX2 = (X.^2)*PX'       % E[X^2]
VX = EX2 - EX^2        % Var[X]
disp(' ')
disp('Use row matrices X and PX for further calculations')
```

●────────────

EXAMPLE 4.5
Use of the Program Simple

Since canonic has given X and PX, we can enter them directly into simple at the prompts.

```
>>simple
Enter row matrix of X-values  X
Enter row matrix PX of X probabilities  PX
EX  =  16.4000
EX2 = 386.0000
VX  = 117.0400
Use row matrices X and PX for further calculations
```

———————————————————————————————●

FUNCTIONS WITH COMPOSITE DEFINITIONS

Often the function g applied to X has a composite definition, in the sense that it is defined differently for different parts of its domain. We consider examples of this sort.

●————————————

EXAMPLE 4.6
Function with Composite Definition

Suppose $X \sim$ binomial $(10, 0.37)$ and

$$g(t) = \begin{cases} t^2 & \text{for } t \leq 3, \text{ or odd and } \geq 5 \\ 3 - t & \text{otherwise} \end{cases}$$

Determine the distribution for $Z = g(X)$ and the expectation $E[Z]$.

```
>>X = 0:10;
>>PX = ibinom(10,0.37,0:10);
>>M = (X <= 3)|((X >= 5)&(rem(X,2) ~= 0))
M = 1   1   1   1   0   1   0   1   0   1   0
>>G = (X.^2).*M + (-X + 3).*(1 - M)
G = 0   1   4   9  -1  25  -3  49  -5  81  -7
>>gdbn
Z is a row matrix of Z = g(X) values
PZ is a row matrix of P(Z=v)
To view the distribution for Z = g(X), call for GDBN
>>GDBN
GDBN =
    -7.0000    0.0000
    -5.0000    0.0063
    -3.0000    0.0849
    -1.0000    0.2461
          0    0.0098
     1.0000    0.0578
     4.0000    0.1529
     9.0000    0.2394
    25.0000    0.1734
```

Continues

```
    49.0000      0.0285
    81.0000      0.0008
>> EZ = G*PX'              % Calculation using g(t) and P(X=t)
EZ = 8.0895
>> EZ = v*PZ'              % Alternate, using v and P(Z=v)
EZ = 8.0895
```

In the next example, we illustrate a practical case of compound definition of the function g and the use of a simple approximation to the Poisson distribution. While the Poisson distribution is defined for nonnegative integers (and hence is discrete), it has an unlimited number of possible values. However, for any value of the parameter μ, there is a point beyond which the probability of larger values is so small that it is negligible. We make a practical determination of such a point by considering a value k for which $P(X \geq k)$ is negligible for calculations at hand.

EXAMPLE 4.7
Optimal Stocking of Merchandise

A merchant is planning for the Christmas season. He intends to stock m units of a certain item at a cost of c per unit. Experience indicates demand can be represented by a random variable $D \sim$ Poisson (μ). If units remain in stock at the end of the season, they may be returned with recovery of r per unit. If demand exceeds the number originally ordered, extra units may be ordered at a cost of s each. Units are sold at a price p per unit.

If $Z = g(D)$ is the gain from the sales, then

For $t \leq m$, $g(t) = (p - c)t - (c - r)(m - t) = (p - r)t + (r - c)m$

For $t > m$, $g(t) = (p - c)m + (t - m)(p - s) = (p - s)t + (s - c)m$

Let $M = (m, \infty)$. Then

$$g(t) = [1 - I_M(t)][(p - r)t + (r - c)m] + I_M(t)[(p - s)t + (s - c)m]$$
$$= (p - r)t - (c - r)m - I_M(t)[(s - r)(t - m)]$$

Suppose $\mu = 50$, $c = 30$, $p = 50$, $r = 20$,   and $s = 40$.   Determine $E[G]$ and $P(G \geq 1000)$. We enter the problem parameters and check the Poisson distribution for an appropriate cutoff point.

_____ MATLAB Script _____

```
>>mu = 50;
>>c = 30;
>>p = 50;
>>r = 20;
>>s = 40;
>>m = 50;
>>test = cpoisson(50,75:25:150)
```

Continues

```
test =
   1.0e-03 *
     0.5778    0.0000    0.0000    0.0000   % A cutoff value of 100 should
                                            % be adequate
>>X = 0:100;
>>PX = [ipoisson(mu,0:99) cpoisson(mu,100)];
>>M = X > m;
>>G = (p - r)*X - (c - r)*m - M*(s - r).*(X - m);
>>gdbn
Z is a row matrix of Z = g(X) values
PZ is a row matrix of P(Z=v)
To view the distribution for Z = g(X), call for GDBN
>>EG = G*PX'
EG = 943.6750
>>A = G >= 1000;
>>PA = A*PX'
PA = 0.5188          % Probability P(g(D) >= 1000)
```

REINFORCEMENT EXERCISES AND EXPLORATION PROBLEMS

REINFORCEMENT EXERCISES

P4.1. Minterm probabilities $p(0)$ through $p(15)$ for the class $\{A, B, C, D\}$ are, in order,

$$0.084 \; 0.196 \; 0.036 \; 0.084 \; 0.085 \; 0.196 \; 0.035 \; 0.084 \cdots$$

$$0.021 \; 0.049 \; 0.009 \; 0.021 \; 0.020 \; 0.049 \; 0.010 \; 0.021$$

Determine the distribution for random variable

$$X = -2.7I_A - 0.5I_B + 3I_C + 7.2I_D - 6.5$$

P4.2. For the minterm probabilities in Problem 1, determine $P(A_{k4})$, $0 \le k \le 4$, where A_{k4} is the event of getting exactly k of the the four events on any trial. *Suggestion:* Use canonic on the random variable $X = I_A + I_B + I_C + I_D$.

P4.3. Use canonic to obtain the binomial coefficients $C(10, k)$. *Suggestion:* Use a random variable similar to the one in the previous problem. Let each $p_k = 1$, $0 \le k \le 2^{10} - 1$.

P4.4. A woman goes shopping for clothing. She considers four items: a pair of shoes at $60, a dress at $125, a sweater at $45, and costume jewelry at $20.

    a. How many different combinations of these items will cost no more than $125?

    b. How many different combinations will cost more than $100?

P4.5. A man is considering four items costing $6, $12, $18, and $24 each. How many ways can he spend $50 or less on these items?

P4.6. Clarence places four bets at a total cost of $45. The payoffs, if he wins, are $25, $30, $25, and $10, with respective probabilities 0.4, 0.6, 0.5, and 0.6. Let E_i be the event of winning the ith bet. Assume the E_i form an independent class.

    a. Express Clarence's net winnings (i.e., the sum of the payoffs minus the amount bet) as a simple random variable X.

    b. Determine the probability distribution for X. What is the probability X is positive?

P4.7. Susan is a member of a cooperative arts and handicraft shop. She places four pots on display in the shop, at a charge of $5 each if sold in six weeks. The selling price of the pots are $25, $35, $30, and $40. The probabilities that they will be sold are 0.6, 0.7, 0.8, and 0.7, respectively. Let E_i be the event the ith pot will sell. Assume the E_i form an independent class.

    a. Express Susan's net income as a simple random variable X.

    b. Determine the probability distribution for X. What is the probability she will take in at least $50 over the cost of selling?

P4.8. A survey of 100 homes in an area is taken to determine the newspaper reading habits of the families. In particular, they are questioned about subscriptions to the daily *Houston Post, Newsweek,* and *Time Magazine.* If A, B, and C are the events of subscribing to the *Post, Newsweek,* and *Time,* respectively, the data indicate the following probabilities:

$$P(A) = 0.70, \qquad P(B) = 0.50, \qquad P(C) = 0.60, \qquad P(AB^c) = 0.30,$$
$$P(BC) = 0.20, \qquad P(A^cC) = 0.30, \qquad P(ABC) = 0.10$$

Suppose a year's subscription to the *Post* is $100, to *Newsweek* is $36, and to *Time* is $40. Then

$$X = 100I_A + 36I_B + 40I_C$$

is the annual amount a family spends on these. Determine the distribution for X, the average value $E[X]$, and the probability $P(X \geq 90)$

P4.9. A simple random variable X has the following distribution:

$t =$	-11.7	-8.3	-3.1	1.2	9.5	14.7	20.1
$P(X = t)$	0.144	0.103	0.094	0.197	0.136	0.154	0.172

Determine $E[X]$, Var$[X]$ and $P(3X^2 - 4X + 2 \geq 250)$. If $Z = X^2 - 20X + 3$, determine the distribution for Z, $P(-20 \leq Z \leq 100)$, $E[Z]$, and Var$[Z]$.

P 4.10 One dimensional random walk. A particle starts at the origin. At successive instants, it moves either one unit to the right or one unit to the left with probability 0.5. Successive moves are independent. Let X_n be the position after n moves. Determine the distribution for X_n, $n = 2, 4, 6, 8, 10$. First, we find an expression for X_n. Let E_i be the event the particle moves to the right on the ith move. Then $Y_n = I_{E_i} - (1 - I_{E_i}) = 2I_{E_i} - 1$ is the amount moved on the ith occasion. Thus,

$$X_n = \sum_{i=1}^{n} Y_i = 2\sum_{i=1}^{n} I_{E_i} - n = 2S_n - n$$

where S_n is the number of right moves in n trials. Note that $S_n \sim$ binomial $(n, 0.5)$.

EXPLORATION PROBLEMS

P4.1 Plotting the distribution function. When the distribution (values and corresponding values) for a simple random variable X are obtained, it is easy to plot the distribution function F_X. Suppose canonic has been used and the matrices X and PX have been obtained. Then the MATLAB command $FX = \text{cumsum}(PX)$ yields a matrix which has values of F_X at each possible value of X. This can be plotted as a step function by the command stairs(X, FX). The character of the graph of F_X can be highlighted by extending the X matrix to one point on each side of the range and extending the FX matrix by assigning zero to the left-hand point and one to the right-hand point. Suppose values of X range from zero to 30. Then the modifications could be made as follows:

$$X = [-1 \; X \; 32]; \quad \text{and} \quad FX = [0 \; FX \; 1];$$

Then the command stairs(X, FX) gives a step graph which has the value zero until the first value of X is reached, and has the value one for a short distance past the largest value of X.

P4.2 Costs with price breaks. Let D be the demand random variable. Suppose there is

A flat fee of C for $D \le a_1$

A cost of c_1 per unit for $a_1 < D \le a_2$

A cost of c_2 per unit for $a_2 < D \le a_3$

A cost of c_3 per unit for $a_3 < D$

Then
$$g(t) = C + c_1 I_{M_1}(t)(t - a_1) + (c_2 - c_1)I_{M_2}(t)(t - a_2)$$
$$+ (c_3 - c_2)I_{M_3}(t)(t - a_3) \quad \text{where } M_i = [a_i, \infty)$$

Note: Since $(t - a_i) = 0$ at $t = a_i$, we could as well have $M_i = (a_i, \infty)$.

If N is Poisson (μ), we may obtain an exact solution for $E[g(X)]$ by using the fact that

$$E[I_{[m,\infty)}(X)] = P(X \ge m) \quad \text{and}$$

$$E[I_{[m,\infty)}(X)X] = e^{-\mu} \sum_{k=m}^{\infty} k\frac{\mu^k}{k!}$$

$$= \mu e^{-\mu} \sum_{k=m-1}^{\infty} \frac{\mu^k}{k!} = \mu P(X \ge m - 1)$$

As an alternate approach, we approximate N by an appropriate number of values and calculate probabilities, expectations, variances, etc. As an example, consider the following:

A residential College is planning a camping trip over Spring Recess. The number X of persons planning to go is assumed to be Poisson (15). Arrangements for transportation and food have been made as follows:

If $X \leq 4$, a minimal flat fee of $450 will be charged

If $4 < X \leq 19$, the additional charge is $100 for each person more than 4 (but less than 20)

If $19 < X$, the charge is $80 for each person past 19

Thus, $C = 450, a_1 = 4, a_2 = 19, c_1 = 100$, and $c_2 = 80$. The distribution for X is Poisson (15). We have

$$Y = g(X) = 450 + 100I_{[4,\infty)}(X)(X - 4) + (80 - 100)I_{[19,\infty)}(X)(X - 19)$$
$$= 450 + 100I_{[4,\infty)}(X)X - 20I_{[19,\infty)}(X)X - 400I_{[4,\infty)}(X) + 380I_{[19,\infty)}(X)$$

a. Obtain the "exact" solution to $E[g(X)]$.
b. Approximate N by terms up to 40 and obtain $E[g(X)]$ and $P(g(X) \geq v$ for $v = 1000, 1500, 2000$, and 2500.

P4.3. For the pattern in Problem 2, work out several break point schedules, perhaps with more break points, and perform the calculations.

P4.4. A game is played with the Bernoulli trial generator (btdata and bt). Each play corresponds to $n = 20$ "trials," with probability p of success. Payoff is made according to the following schedule:

No. of Successes	0–5	6–10	11–15	16–20
Payoff	$5.00	$10.00	$15.00	$20.00

Adjust p so that the expected payoff is approximately $10.00 (plus or minus a few cents). What is the variance of the payoff? What happens if the probability p of success is doubled? Does the expected payoff double? Now adjust p so the the expected gain is approximately $15.00. How does this compare with p for $10.00 expected gain? Would it be instructive to tabulate (or plot) expected gain versus probability p? Can you anticipate the shape of such a curve?

Jointly Distributed Simple
Random Variables

PREVIEW

We extend the calculation techniques for simple random variables to a pair of jointly distributed simple random variables. The distribution is expressed in a matrix P with elements $P(X = t, Y = u)$ and two row matrices with the ranges of X and Y, respectively. The probabilities in P are arranged as on the plane. The principal device enabling extension of single-variable methods is the formulation of two special matrices t and u with values of X and Y in the proper positions to match with the corresponding joint probabilities. With the matrices P, t, and u, we may use relational and array operations, as in the one variable case.

1. EXTENSION OF SINGLE-VARIABLE TECHNIQUES

We examine calculations on a pair of simple random variables $\{X, Y\}$ considered jointly. These are, in effect, two components of a random vector $W = (X, Y)$, which maps from the basic space Ω to the plane. The induced probability distribution is on the (t, u)-plane. Values on the horizontal axis (t-axis) correspond to values of the first coordinate random variable X and values on the vertical axis (u-axis) correspond to values of Y. We extend the computational strategy used for a single random variable.

A REVIEW OF SINGLE-VARIABLE TECHNIQUES

First, let us review the one-variable strategy. There are two basic kinds of calculations. Data consist of values t_i and corresponding probabilities

$P(X = t_i)$ arranged in matrices

$$X = [t_1, t_2, \cdots, t_n] \quad \text{and} \quad PX = [p_1, p_2, \cdots, p_n] \quad \text{where } p_i = P(X = t_i)$$

1. $P(g(X) \in M)$, where M is some prescribed set of values.
   a. Determine the *positions* for which $g(t_i) \in M$. To do this, use relational operations to determine a positional matrix M.
   b. Select the $P(X = t_i)$ in the corresponding positions and sum. This is accomplished by the MATLAB operation $M * PX'$ or, equivalently, $\text{sum}(M. * PX)$.
2. $E[g(X)] = \sum_{i=1}^{n} g(t_i)P(X = t_i)$.
   a. Form a matrix $G = [g(t_1) \; g(t_2) \cdots g(t_n)]$ which has $g(t_i)$ in a position corresponding to $p_i = P(X = t_i)$ in matrix PX. This is accomplished by array operations on X.
   b. Multiply each $g(t_i)$ by the corresponding p_i and sum. This is accomplished by the MATLAB operation $G * PX'$.

THE *t* AND *u* MATRICES

The joint distribution for a pair $\{X, Y\}$ of simple random variables consists of probability mass concentrations $P(X = t_i, Y = u_j)$ at points (t_i, u_j) on the plane. The joint probability is represented by a matrix P with elements corresponding to the mass points on the plane. We put X-values in a row matrix $X = [t_1 \; t_2 \cdots t_n]$ and Y-values in $Y = [u_1 \; u_2 \cdots u_m]$. The two basic problems are

1. $P(g(X, Y) \in M)$, where M is some prescribed set of points on the plane.
   a. Determine the *positions* for which $g(t_i, u_j) \in M$. To do this, use relational operations to determine a positional matrix M.
   b. Select the $P(X = t_i, Y = u_j)$ in the corresponding positions and sum. This is accomplished by the MATLAB operation $\text{sum}(\text{sum}(M. * P))$.
2. $E[g(X, Y)] = \sum_{i,j} g(t_i, u_j)P(X = t_i, Y = u_j)$.
   a. Form a matrix G whose elements $g(t_i, u_j)$ are in the same positions as the corresponding $P(X = t_i, Y = u_j)$.
   b. Multiply corresponding pairs $g(t_i, u_j)$, $P(X = t_i, Y = u_j)$ and sum all products. This is accomplished by the MATLAB operation $\text{sum}(\text{sum}(G. * P))$.

The matrix P with elements $P(X = t_i, Y = u_j)$ in the normal matrix formulation would have each such element on row i and column j. However, for positions as on the plane, this element is in the ith column and in the jth row *from the bottom*. Also, it is necessary to have values of $(X, Y) = (t_i, u_j)$ in the proper positions.

1. To get values of X in the necessary positions, we form a matrix t in which the elements of the ith column are all t_i. This means that t consists of m rows of the set of X values in normal order.
2. To get values of Y in the correct positions, we form a matrix u with the jth row *from the bottom* having u_j in all positions. This means that u consists of n columns of Y values in the desired order (i.e., increasing upward).
3. Array operations on the matrices t and u are used to obtain the desired matrix G with elements $g(t_i, u_j)$ in the proper places.
4. Relational operations on matrix G are used to determine those positions in which the $g(t_i, u_j)$ satisfy the prescribed criteria.

MARGINAL DISTRIBUTIONS FOR *X* AND *Y*

The marginal distribution for X is obtained by summing the columns in P. For this we use the MATLAB function sum. Thus, $PX = \text{sum}(P)$. If we apply the sum function to the transpose P', we get the row sums which are elements of the matrix PY. Because of the reversal, with probabilities corresponding to the largest value of Y first, we need to reverse the order to obtain PY.

The following MATLAB procedure takes the data in matrices X, Y, and P and forms the matrices t and u. For purposes of illustration, it displays the t, u, and P matrices and the matrices derived therefrom. Also, it determines the marginal probabilities for X and Y. An alternate working version *jaclc* suppresses the intermediate details, which ordinarily are not of interest.

——————————— MATLAB Script ———————————

```
% file jcalcd.m
% Version of 10/4/93
disp('Setup for calculations for joint simple random variables')
disp(' ')
disp('Matrix P has joint probabilities arranged as on the plane')
disp('  X-values horizontally, left to right')
disp('  Y-values vertically, increasing upward')
P = input('Enter matrix P  ')
X = input('Enter row matrix of values of X   ')
Y = input('Enter row matrix of values of Y   ')
n = length(X)           % dimension of X
m = length(Y)           % dimension of Y
PX = sum(P)             % probabilities for X
PY = fliplr(sum(P'))    % probabilities for Y
t = ones(m,1)*X         % m rows of X       (m x n)
u = rot90(Y)*ones(1,n)  % n columns of Y (values increasing upward) (m x n)
disp(' Use array operations on matrices X, Y, PX, PY, t, u, and P')
```

EXAMPLE 5.1

Basic Calculations

————————————————————— MATLAB Script —————————————————

```
>> jdemo3              % Call for data
>> jcalcd
Setup for calculations for joint simple random variables
Matrix P has joint probabilities arranged as on the plane
  X-values horizontally, left to right
  Y-values vertically, increasing upward
Enter matrix P   P
P  =  0.0132     0.0198     0.0297     0.0209     0.0264
      0.0372     0.0558     0.0837     0.0589     0.0744
      0.0516     0.0774     0.1161     0.0817     0.1032
      0.0180     0.0270     0.0405     0.0285     0.0360
Enter row matrix of values of X   X
X  = -4      -2      0      1      3
Enter row matrix of values of Y   Y
Y  =  0       1      2      4
n  =  5
m  =  4
PX = 0.1200     0.1800     0.2700     0.1900     0.2400
PY = 0.1500     0.4300     0.3100     0.1100
t  = -4      -2      0      1      3
     -4      -2      0      1      3
     -4      -2      0      1      3
     -4      -2      0      1      3
u  =  4       4      4      4      4
      2       2      2      2      2
      1       1      1      1      1
      0       0      0      0      0
Use array operations on matrices X, Y, PX, PY, t, u, and P
>> G = t.^2 - 3*u
G  =  4      -8     -12    -11     -3
     10      -2      -6     -5      3
     13       1      -3     -2      6
     16       4       0      1      9
>> M = G >= 1
M  =  1       0      0      0      0
      1       0      0      0      1
      1       1      0      0      1
      1       1      0      1      1
>> PM = sum(sum(M.*P))
PM =  0.4665
>> EZ = sum(sum(G.*P))
EZ =  0.5200
```

A TEST FOR THE VALIDITY OF A JOINT PROBABILITY MATRIX

If a joint probability matrix P is large, it may be difficult to tell from inspection whether or not it is a valid distribution. Two points need to be checked. First, are there any negative entries? Second, do the entries add to one? The following simple test function performs these checks.

————————————— MATLAB Script —————————————

```
function y=jdtest(P)
% Tests joint probability matrix
% Version of 10/8/93
M = min(min(P));
S = sum(sum(P));
if M < 0
  y = 'Negative entries';
elseif abs(1 - S) > 1e-7
  y = 'Probabilities do not sum to one';
else
  y = 'P is a valid distribution';
end
```

EXAMPLE 5.2
Matrix Test

We test the matrix P in Example 5.1 and make some modifications to force the two invalid cases. The matrix is in the file jdemo3.m.

————————————— MATLAB Script —————————————

```
>> jdemo3
>> jdtest(P)
ans
P is a valid distribution
>> jdtest(P+0.01)
ans =
Probabilities do not sum to one
>> jdtest(P-0.014)
ans =
Negative entries
```

2. CALCULATION OF STANDARD PARAMETERS FOR JOINT DISTRIBUTIONS

We use the procedures established above to calculate basic quantities and parameters associated with the joint distribution for a pair of simple random variables $\{X, Y\}$. Once the operations are worked out, we combine them into a single program. To illustrate the calculation procedures, we use the program jcalc to form the PX, PY, t, and u matrices for a set of data. We use the same data as in Example 5.1.

● ━━━━━━━

EXAMPLE 5.3
Joint Distribution

We use jcalc to form the matrices used in the operations below.

━━━━━━━━━━━━━━━━━━ MATLAB Script ━━━━━━━━━━━━━━━━━━

```
>> jdemo6              % Call for a set of data
>> jcalc               % Call for the program
Setup for calculations for joint simple random variables
Matrix P has joint probabilities arranged as on the plane
  X-values horizontally, left to right
  Y-values vertically, increasing upward
Enter matrix P   P
Enter row matrix of values of X   X
Enter row matrix of values of Y   Y
Use array operations on matrices X, Y, PX, PY, t, u, and P
```

Having used jcalc to form the matrices t and u and to obtain the marginal distributions for X and Y, we may perform a variety of calculations.

MARGINAL DISTRIBUTIONS

The marginal distributions are calculated by jcalc and simply need to be called for. For the example under study, we have

━━━━━━━━━━━━━━━━━━ MATLAB Script ━━━━━━━━━━━━━━━━━━

```
>> PX
PX =   0.1200    0.3590    0.2710    0.1800    0.0700
>> PY
PY =   0.1410    0.2200    0.4180    0.2210
```

EXPECTATION FOR *X* AND *Y*

We have two elementary approaches.

1. Use the marginal distributions: $E[X] = \sum_{i=1}^{n} t_i P(X = t_i)$
2. Use the joint distribution: at each position, multiply the X-value by the joint probability, then sum. To do this we may multiply each element in the t matrix by the corresponding probability in the P matrix, then sum. Since each element in the ith column of the t matrix is the ith

X-value, the result is the same as summing the *i*th column of the *P* matrix then multiplying by the *X*-value.

Similar calculations are made for $E[Y]$. The MATLAB calculations for the example are

─────────────── MATLAB Script ───────────────

```
>> EX = X*PX'                % Calculation with marginals
EX  = 0.0610
>> EY = Y*PY'
EY  = 1.2970
>> EXa = sum(sum(t.*P))      % Alternate calculation with t, P
EXa = 0.0610
>> EYa = sum(sum(u.*P))
EYa = 1.2970
```

───

VARIANCE

The variances are $\text{Var}[X] = E[X^2] - E[X]^2$ and $\text{Var}[Y] = E[Y^2] - E[Y]^2$. Again, we have alternate calculations of $E[X^2]$ and $E[Y^2]$. The calculations for $\text{Var}[X]$ are

─────────────── MATLAB Script ───────────────

```
>> EX2 = (X.^2)*PX'
EX2  = 4.6790
>> EX2a = sum(sum((t.^2).*P))
EX2a = 4.6790
>> VX = EX2 - EX^2
VX   = 4.6753
```

───

COVARIANCE

The quantity $\text{Cov}[X, Y] = E[XY] - E[X]E[Y]$. Having $E[X]$ and $E[Y]$, we need only calculate $E[XY]$.

─────────────── MATLAB Script ───────────────

```
>> EXY = sum(sum(t.*u.*P))
EXY  = 0.1770
>> CV = EXY - EX*EY
CV   = 0.0979
```

THE REGRESSION LINE OF *Y* ON *X*

The regression line of Y on X is of the form $u = at + b$, where $a = \text{Cov}[X, Y]/\text{Var}[X]$ and $b = E[Y] - aE[X]$. Since we have all the values needed, the combination is straightforward.

———————————— MATLAB Script ————————————

```
>> a = CV/VX
a  =  0.0209
>> b = EY - a*EX
b  =  1.2957
```

CONDITIONAL EXPECTATION *E[Y|X = x]*

An elementary treatment of conditional expectation in the simple random variable case shows that $E[Y \mid X = t_i]$ is expectation of Y with respect to the conditional probability distribution:

$$P(Y = u_j \mid X = t_i) \qquad 1 \leq j \leq m$$

In terms of the probability mass distribution on the plane, the conditional expectation, given $X = t_i$, is the center of mass of that part of the joint distribution above the point t_i on the real line. We may express this as

$$E[Y \mid X = t_i] = \sum_{j=1}^{m} u_j P(Y = u_j \mid X = t_i)$$

$$= \sum_{j=1}^{m} u_j P(Y = u_j, zX = t_i)/P(X = t_i)$$

We obtain the conditional expectation for each possible value of X in one simple MATLAB operation.

———————————— MATLAB Script ————————————

```
>> eYx = sum(u.*P)./sum(P)      % E[Y|X=x] for x = -3, -1, 0, 2, 6,
                                % respectively
eYx = 0.3000    1.7521    1.5683    0.4556    1.7857
```

3. FUNCTIONS OF A PAIR OF RANDOM VARIABLES *X, Y*

———————————— ■ ————————————

DISTRIBUTION FOR *Z = g (X, Y)*

As in the single-variable case, we may utilize array operations on matrices t and u to obtain a matrix G whose elements are $g(t_i, u_j)$.

EXAMPLE 5.4

Matrix for a
Function

Obtain the matrix G for the function

$$g(t, u) = tu^2 - 3t + 5u$$

———————————————— MATLAB Script ————————————————

```
>> G = t.*(u.^2) - 3*t + 5*u;    % Function as array operations
```

To obtain the distribution for $Z = g(X, Y)$, we may use the following procedure, based on the csort function.

———————————————— MATLAB Script ————————————————

```
% file jgdbn.m
% Determines distribution for Z = g(X,Y)
% Version of 5/10/93
% Assumes  P = joint probability matrix
%          G  = matrix of g(t,u)
%          Procedure csort
GDBN = csort(G(:)',P(:)')';
Z  =  GDBN(:,1)';
PZ = GDBN(:,2)';
disp('Z  is a row matrix of Z = g(X,Y) values')
disp('PZ is a row matrix of P(Z=z)')
disp('To view the distribution for Z = g(X,Y), call for GDBN')
disp('To determine E[g(X,Y)|X=x], call for ezx')
```

EXAMPLE 5.5

Continuation of
Example 5.4

———————————————— MATLAB Script ————————————————

```
>> G = t.*(u.^2) - 3*t + 5*u;           % g(t,u) = tu^2 - 3t + 5u
>> jgdbn
Z  is a row matrix of Z = g(X,Y) values  % These quantities are in
PZ is a row matrix of P(Z=z)             % the MATLAB workspace
To view the distribution for Z = g(X,Y), call for GDBN
To determine E[g(X,Y)|X=x], call for ezx
>> disp(GDBN)                            % Optional call for display
   -33.0000    0.0400
   -21.0000    0.0150
   -19.0000    0.0230
   -18.0000    0.0120
   -15.0000    0.0370
```

Continues

-6.0000	0.0650
-3.0000	0.0380
0	0.0280
3.0000	0.0900
7.0000	0.1150
9.0000	0.1960
10.0000	0.1440
12.0000	0.0560
16.0000	0.0150
20.0000	0.0620
21.0000	0.0110
46.0000	0.0210
98.0000	0.0320

CONDITIONAL EXPECTATION $E[Y|X=x]$

If we have a function $Z = g(X, Y)$, it may be desirable to calculate the conditional expectation, given X. Once the matrix $G = g(t, u)$ is set up by jgdbn, we may use the following:

_____ MATLAB Script _____

```
% file ezx.m
% Determines E[Z|X = t] for Z = g(X,Y)
% Version of 2/10/93
% Assumes  P = joint probability matrix
%          G = matrix of g(t,u)
%          X = matrix of X values
eZx = sum(G.*P)./sum(P);
EZX = [X; eZx]';
disp('E[g(X,y)|X=x] is in eZx; to view, call for EZX')
```

EXAMPLE 5.6
Continuation of Examples 5.4 and 5.5

_____ MATLAB Script _____

```
>> ezx
E[g(X,y)|X=x] is in eZx; to view, call for EZX
disp(EZX)
    -3.0000   -10.9000
    -1.0000     5.7799
          0     7.8413
     2.0000     6.3000
     6.0000    48.4429
```

—■—

If the pair $\{X, Y\}$ is independent, then fewer data are required and the computations are simpler. Independence for simple random variables is characterized by the product rule:

$$P(X = t_i, Y = u_j) = P(X = t_i)P(Y = u_j) \qquad 1 \le i \le n,\ 1 \le j \le m$$

As a consequence, we need only the marginal distributions to obtain the complete joint distribution. We begin by developing a simple MATLAB function *idbn* for obtaining the joint distribution from the marginals. We use that function as an element in several procedures. A procedure *ijdbn* which prompts for inputs of marginal probabilities uses idbn to form the joint probability matrix. A procedure *itest* is developed to test a joint distribution for independence. We incorporate the test into a general procedure jsimple for jointly distributed random variables. Also, we develop a general procedure *isimple* for an independent pair of simple random variables. From the input marginal probabilities we use idbn to form the joint probability matrix.

First, we consider:

—————————————— MATLAB Script ——————————————

```
function y=idbn(px,py)
% Version of 9/11/93
n = length(px);
m = length(py);
a = ones(m,1)*px;          % Rows identical to px
b = rot90(py)*ones(1,n);   % Columns identical to py (as on the plane)
y = a.*b;                  % Matrix of joint independent probabilities
```

A procedure based on this operation prompts for inputs, then calculates the joint probability matrix.

—————————————— MATLAB Script ——————————————

```
% ijdbn.m
% Version of 9/11/93
% Assumes function idbn
disp(' Joint distribution for two independent, simple')
disp(' random variables (arranged as on the plane)')
PX = input('Enter X probabilities  ');
PY = input('Enter Y probabilities  ');
PI = idbn(PX,PY);
disp(' ')
disp('    Matrix PI of joint probabilities')
disp(PI)
```

EXAMPLE 5.7

Independent
Distribution

```
>> PX = 0.1*[2 1 4 3];
>> PY = 0.01*[30 25 45];
>> ijdbn
 Joint distribution for two independent, simple
 random variables (arranged as on the plane)
 Enter X probabilities   PX
 Enter Y probabilities   PY
    Matrix PI of joint probabilities
       0.0900    0.0450    0.1800    0.1350
       0.0500    0.0250    0.1000    0.0750
       0.0600    0.0300    0.1200    0.0900
```

The function idbn is also made the basis of a test of the joint distribution for independence. We determine the marginals from the matrix *P* for the joint distribution. From the marginals we construct a test matrix for which the product rule holds. This is compared with the original matrix.

—————————————— MATLAB Script ——————————

```
% file itest.m
% Version of 1/5/94
% Assumes the function idbn
disp('Tests matrix of joint probabilities for')
disp('a simple pair {X,Y} for independence.')
P = input('Enter matrix of joint probabilities  ');
disp(' ')
px = sum(P);                 % Marginal probabilities for X
py = fliplr(sum(P'));        % Marginal probabilities for Y
PT = idbn(px,py);            % Matrix of joint independent
                             % probabilities
D  = abs(P - PT) > 1e-9;     % Threshold set above roundoff
if total(D) > 0
  disp('The pair {X,Y} is NOT independent')
else
  disp('The pair {X,Y} is independent')
end
disp(' ')
disp('To see where product rule fails, call for D')
disp(' ')
```

EXAMPLE 5.8

Use of itest

```
>> idemo1    % Call for matrix in file idemo1.m
>> itest
```

Continues

CHAPTER 5

```
           Tests matrix of joint probabilities for
           a simple pair {X,Y} for independence.
           Enter matrix of joint probabilities P
           The pair {X,Y} is NOT independent
           To see where product rule fails, call for D
           >> D
           D =  0     0     0     0     0     0     0
                0     0     0     0     0     0     0
                0     0     0     0     0     0     0
                1     1     1     1     1     1     1
                0     0     0     0     0     0     0
                0     0     0     0     0     0     0
                0     0     0     0     0     0     0
                1     1     1     1     1     1     1
                0     0     0     0     0     0     0
                0     0     0     0     0     0     0
                0     0     0     0     0     0     0
                0     0     0     0     0     0     0
```

The matrix *P* and the test matrix *PT* are not normally displayed. In this case, there are many places where the two agree. However, if they fail to agree in any one or more places, the random variables do not form an independent pair.

Next, we consider an example in which the pair is independent.

EXAMPLE 5.9

Independent Pair

———————————————— MATLAB Script ————————————————

```
>> jdemo3      % call for data in m-file
>> P           % call to display P
P =  0.0132    0.0198    0.0297    0.0209    0.0264
     0.0372    0.0558    0.0837    0.0589    0.0744
     0.0516    0.0774    0.1161    0.0817    0.1032
     0.0180    0.0270    0.0405    0.0285    0.0360
>> itest
Tests matrix of joint probabilities for
a simple pair {X,Y} for independence.
Enter matrix of joint probabilities  P
The pair {X,Y} is independent
To see where product rule fails, call for D
>> D
D =  0     0     0     0     0
     0     0     0     0     0
     0     0     0     0     0
     0     0     0     0     0
```

5. GENERAL PROCEDURES FOR SIMPLE RANDOM VARIABLES

■

THE PROCEDURE jsimple

We gather into one procedure the setup procedure of jcalc, the test for independence, and automatic calculation of $E[X]$, $E[Y]$, Var$[X]$, Var$[Y]$, Cov$[X, Y]$, the coefficients for the regression line, the correlation coefficient ρ, and $E[Y \mid X = x]$ for all values of X. Additionaly, the t, u, X, Y, PX, PY, and P matrices are available for further calculations.

_____ MATLAB Script _____

```
% jsimple.m
% file jsimple.m
% Version of 12/14/93
disp('Calculates basic quantities for jointly distributed')
disp('simple random variables')
disp(' ')
disp('Matrix P has joint probabilities arranged as on the plane')
disp('  X-values horizontally, left to right')
disp('  Y-values vertically, increasing upward')
P = input('Enter matrix P  ');
X = input('Enter row matrix of X-values  ');
Y = input('Enter row matrix of Y-values  ');
disp(' ')
n = length(X);        % dimension of X
m = length(Y);        % dimension of Y
PX = sum(P);          % marginal distribution for X
PY = fliplr(sum(P')); % marginal distribution for Y
XDBN = [X; PX]';
YDBN = [Y; PY]';
PT = idbn(PX,PY);
D = sum(sum(abs(P - PT))); % test for difference
if D > 1e-8            % to prevent roundoff error masking zero
  disp('{X,Y} is NOT independent')
 else
  disp('{X,Y} is independent')
end
disp(' ')
t = ones(m,1)*X;           % m rows of X    (m x n)
u = rot90(Y)*ones(1,n);    % n columns of Y (increasing upward)  (m x n)
EX  = sum(sum(t.*P))       % E[X]
EY  = sum(sum(u.*P))       % E[Y]
EX2 = sum(sum((t.^2).*P))  % E[X^2]
EY2 = sum(sum((u.^2).*P))  % E[Y^2]
```

Continues

```
EXY = sum(sum(t.*u.*P))        % E[XY]
VX  = EX2 - EX^2               % Var[X]
VY  = EY2' - EY^2              % Var[Y]
cv = EXY - EX*EY;              % Cov[X,Y] = E[XY] - E[X]E[Y]
if abs(cv) > 1e-9  % to prevent roundoff error masking zero
   CV = cv
  else
   CV = 0
end
a = CV/VX                      % regression line of Y on X is
b = EY - a*EX                  %        u = at + b
R = CV/sqrt(VX*VY);            % correlation coefficient rho
disp(['The regression line of Y on X is:  u = ',num2str(a),'t
+ ',num2str(b),])
disp(['The correlation coefficient is:  rho = ',num2str(R),])
disp(' ')
eYx = sum(u.*P)./PX;
EYX = [X;eYx]';
disp('Marginal dbns are in X, PX, Y, PY; to view, call XDBN, YDBN')
disp('E[Y|X = x] is in eYx; to view, call for EYX')
disp('Use array operations on matrices X, Y, PX, PY, t, u, and P')
```

●────────

EXAMPLE 5.10
*Combined Use of
jsimple, jgdbn, and
ezx*

─────────────────── MATLAB Script ───────────────────

```
>> jdemo1
>> jsimple
Calculates basic quantities for jointly distributed
simple random variables
Matrix P has joint probabilities arranged as on the plane
  X-values horizontally, left to right
  Y-values vertically, increasing upward
Enter matrix P  P
Enter row matrix of X-values  X
Enter row matrix of Y-values  Y
{X,Y} is not independent
EX  =  0.6420
EY  =  0.0783
EX2 =  3.7137
EY2 =  3.6627
EXY = -0.1130
VX  =  3.3016
VY  =  3.6566
CV  = -0.1633
```

Continues

```
a    = -0.0494
b    =  0.1100
The regression line of Y on X is:  u = -0.0494t + 0.11
The correlation coefficient is:   rho = -0.0470
Marginal dbns are in X, PX, Y, PY; to view, call XDBN, YDBN
E[Y|X = x] is in eYx; to view, call for EYX
Use array operations on matrices X, Y, PX, PY, t, u, and P
>> disp(XDBN)
    -2.3700    0.1038
    -1.9300    0.0525
    -0.4700    0.1151
    -0.1100    0.1065
          0    0.1328
     0.5700    0.0918
     1.2200    0.0986
     2.1500    0.1000
     2.9700    0.0992
     3.7400    0.0997
>> disp(YDBN)
    -3.0600    0.1659
    -1.4400    0.0997
    -1.2100    0.1167
     0.0700    0.1303
     0.8800    0.1348
     1.7700    0.1406
     2.0100    0.1301
     2.8400    0.0819
>> disp(EYX)
    -2.3700   -0.2640
    -1.9300   -0.0455
    -0.4700    0.6833
    -0.1100    0.4775
          0    0.2072
     0.5700    0.2561
     1.2200   -0.4129
     2.1500    0.1386
     2.9700   -0.4849
     3.7400    0.0250
>> Q = t.^2 + u.^2 > 4;
>> pQ = sum(sum(Q.*P))
pQ  =  0.6732
>> G = (t.^2).*(1 - Q) + 3*Q;
>> jgdbn
Z  is a row matrix of Z = g(X,Y) values    % These quantities are in
PZ is a row matrix of P(Z=z)               % the MATLAB workspace
To view the distribution for Z = g(X,Y), call for GDBN
To determine E[g(X,Y)|X=x], call for ezx
```

Continues

CHAPTER 5

```
>> disp(GDBN)
          0        0.0745
     0.0121       0.0520
     0.2209       0.0740
     0.3249       0.0689
     1.4884       0.0572
     3.0000       0.6732
     3.7249       0.0002
>> ezx
E[g(X,y)|X=x] is in eZx; to view, call for EZX
disp(EZX)
    -2.3700       3.0000
    -1.9300       3.0028
    -0.4700       1.2133
    -0.1100       1.5411
          0       1.3170
     0.5700       0.9922
     1.2200       2.1231
     2.1500       3.0000
     2.9700       3.0000
     3.7400       3.0000
>> EZ = v*PZ'            % Calculation from Z distribution
EZ  =  2.1448
>> Ez = sum(sum(G.*P))   % Calculation from joint distribution
Ez  =  2.1448
>> Eza = eZx*PX'         % Use of law of total probability
Eza =  2.1448
>> M = (v >= 3)|(v <= 1);
>> PM = M*PZ'            % Calculation using Z distribution
PM  =  0.9428
>> N = (G >= 3)|(G <= 1);
>> Pm = sum(sum(N.*P))   % Calculation using joint distribution
Pm  =  0.9428
```

THE PROCEDURE isimple

As a consequence of the product rule for independent simple random variables, we need only the marginal distributions to determine the joint distribution. Also, independence implies the variables are uncorrelated and $E[Y \mid X = x] = E[Y]$ for all possible values of X. It is therefore desirable to have a special procedure for independent simple random variables.

—————————— MATLAB Script ——————————

```
% isimple.m
% file isimple.m
% version of 9/11/93
```

Continues

```
disp('Calculations for independent simple random variables')
disp('   X-values horizontally, left to right')
disp('   Y-values vertically, increasing upward')
disp('   Marginal probabilities similarly oriented')
X  = input('Enter row matrix of X-values  ');
Y  = input('Enter row matrix of Y-values  ');
PX = input('Enter X probabilities  ');
PY = input('Enter Y probabilities  ');
P  =  idbn(PX,PY);
t  = ones(length(Y),1)*X;         % m rows of X
u  = rot90(Y)*ones(1,length(X)); % n columns of Y (increasing upward)
EX  = X*PX'         % E[X]
EY  = Y*PY'         % E[Y]
EX2 = (X.^2)*PX';    % E[X^2]
EY2 = (Y.^2)*PY';    % E[Y^2]
VX  = EX2 - EX^2     % Var[X]
VY  = EY2' - EY^2    % Var[Y]
disp(' Use array operations on matrices X, Y, PX, PY, t, u, and P')
```

● ────────────

EXAMPLE 5.11

Use of isimple

──────────── MATLAB Script ────────────

```
>> isimple
Calculations for independent simple random variables
   X-values horizontally, left to right
   Y-values vertically, increasing upward
   Marginal probabilities similarly oriented
Enter row matrix of X-values  -2:2
Enter X probabilities  0.1*[1 2 3 2 2]
Enter row matrix of Y-values  -1:2
Enter Y probabilities  0.1*[4 3 2 1]
EX =  0.2000
EY =  0
VX =  1.5600
VY =  1
Use array operations on matrices X, Y, PX, PY, t, u, and P
 For Z = g(X,Y), determine matrix G = [g(ti,uj)]
 Use jgdbn to determine distribution for Z
>> G = 3*t + 2*(u.^2);
>> jgdbn
Z is a row matrix of Z = g(X,Y) values
PZ is a row matrix of P(Z=z)
To view the distribution for Z = g(X,Y), call for GDBN:
To determine E[g(X,Y)|X=x], call for ezx
>> disp(GDBN)
     -6.0000    0.0300
     -4.0000    0.0600
```

Continues

JOINTLY DISTRIBUTED SIMPLE RANDOM VARIABLES

```
   -3.0000     0.0600
   -1.0000     0.1200
         0     0.0900
    2.0000     0.1900
    3.0000     0.0600
    5.0000     0.1400
    6.0000     0.0600
    8.0000     0.1500
   11.0000     0.0200
   14.0000     0.0200
>> ezx
E[g(X,y)|X=x] is in eZx; to view, call for EZX
disp(EZX)
   -2.0000    -4.0000
   -1.0000    -1.0000
         0     2.0000
    1.0000     5.0000
    2.0000     8.0000
```

The general procedures jsimple and isimple perform the basic calculations for a jointly distributed random variables. When a matrix G of values of $g(t, u)$ is set up, the procedures jgdbn and ezx determine the distribution and the conditional expectation, respectively. In the next chapter, we consider how simple approximations can be set up for either a single continuous distribution or for a joint continuous distribution. Then calculations on the discrete approximations are carried out in a manner quite similar to the above.

REINFORCEMENT EXERCISES AND EXPLORATION PROBLEMS

REINFORCEMENT EXERCISES

P5.1 The pair $\{X, Y\}$ has the joint distribution below:

$$P(X = t, \ Y = u)$$

$t =$	-2	-1	0	1	3	5
$u = 4$	0.0338	0.0724	0.0572	0.0488	0.0322	0.0156
3	0.0429	0.0957	0.0726	0.0594	0.0396	0.0198
1	0.0312	0.0696	0.0528	0.0432	0.0288	0.0144
-2	0.0221	0.0523	0.0374	0.0286	0.0194	0.0102

Use jcalc, jgdbn, ezx, and itest, as appropriate to determine the following; then check using jsimple and the others as needed.

a. The marginal distributions for X and Y.
b. Is the pair $\{X, Y\}$ independent?
c. $E[X]$, $E[Y]$, $E[X^2]$, $E[X^2 + 2Y - 3]$, and $P(3X - Y > 0)$ (be careful about inequalities).
d. The regression *line* of Y on X and the conditional expectation $E[Y \mid X = t]$.
e. Let

$$Z = \begin{cases} 2X^2 + Y & \text{for } X > 2Y \\ XY & \text{for } X \le 2Y \end{cases}$$

Determine $E[Z]$ and $E\{Z \mid X = t\}$

P5.2 Repeat the previous problem for the pair with joint distribution:

$$P(X = t, \ Y = u)$$

$t =$	-2.1	-0.9	0	2.7	3.4	5.1
$u = 7.2$	0.0200	0.0150	0.0040	0.0460	0.0100	0.0550
5.6	0.0380	0.0590	0.0380	0.0290	0.0290	0.0300
4.2	0.0460	0.0440	0.0530	0.0140	0.0540	0.0310
1.0	0.0600	0.0450	0.0160	0.0170	0.0550	0.0190
-3.3	0.0220	0.0390	0.0260	0.0220	0.0040	0.0600

P5.3 The pair $\{X, Y\}$ has the joint distribution below:

$$P(X = t, \ Y = u)$$

$t=$	-11.7	-8.3	3.1	1.2	9.5	14.7	20.1
$u=10.8$	0.012	0.022	0.030	0.024	0.030	0.051	0.019
5.6	0.003	0.029	0.038	0.039	0.005	0.043	0.036
2.8	0.038	0.047	0	0.033	0.037	0.015	0.043
-1.7	0.038	0.002	0.022	0.053	0.024	0.003	0.056
-3.9	0.053	0.003	0.004	0.048	0.040	0.042	0.018

a. Determine the marginal distributions for X and Y and the parameters $E[X]$, $E[Y]$, and $\text{Var}[X]$. Is $\{X, Y\}$ an independent pair? Determine $P(X > Y)$.
b. If the value $X(\omega) = -3.1$ is observed, what is the best *linear* estimate, in the mean-square sense, of the corresponding $Y(\omega)$. Compare this with the *best mean-square estimate* for $Y(\omega)$.
c. Let

$$W = \begin{cases} 2X^2 + 3XY & \text{for } Y \ge X \\ 5X^2 & \text{for } Y < X \end{cases}$$

Determine the expectation $E[W]$ (a constant) and the value of the conditional expectation $E[W \mid X = x]$ for each possible value of X.

P5.4 The pair $\{X, Y\}$ is independent, with the following marginal distributions:

$t =$	-11.7	-8.3	-3.1	1.2	9.5	14.7	20.1
$P(X = t)$	0.144	0.103	0.094	0.197	0.136	0.154	0.172

$u =$	-3.9	-1.7	2.8	5.6	10.8
$P(Y = u)$	0.208	0.198	0.213	0.193	0.188

1. Determine the joint distribution and calculate $P(X > Y)$. Compare with the result in the previous problem.
2. Determine $E[X]$, $E[Y]$, $\text{Var}[X]$, and $\text{Var}[Y]$.
3. Why is it not useful to calculate $E[Y \mid X = t]$?
4. Let

$$W = \begin{cases} 2X^2 + 3XY & \text{for } Y \geq X \\ 5X^2 & \text{for } Y < X \end{cases}$$

Determine the expectation $E[W]$ and the conditional expectation $E[W \mid X = x]$ for each possible value of X. Why do these differ from the results in the previous problem?

EXPLORATION PROBLEMS

P5.1 Form a random 5 by 7 matrix P. Check it with the procedure jdtest. Then divide each element by the total of the elements in P and reapply the jdtest. This indicates a simple and convenient way of generating joint probability distributions for pairs of simple random variables.

P5.2 Consider again the compound Bernoulli trials in Example 2.22 (the basketball freethrow contest). Let X be the number of freethrows Mary makes and Y the number that Bill makes. The distributions are binomial, and they represent an independent pair. Use the techniques of this chapter to determine $P(X > Y)$ and compare with those found in Chapter 2. Also do the modified problem.

P5.3 Version 4.1 of MATLAB has a function meshgrid which may be used to set up the t and u matrices, except that values of u increase in the downward direction. This can be corrected with flipud command. To test your understanding of the procedure jcalc (and jsimple), write out a version of jcalc using the meshgrid function.

Discrete Approximation to Continuous Random Variables

PREVIEW

Bounded random variables can be approximated as closely as desired by simple random variables. In fact, a real random variable X may be represented as the limit of a sequence of simple random variables. The integral theory of mathematical expectation is achieved by considering mathematical expectation $E[X]$ as the limit of the expectations of the approximating simple random variables. The latter, of course, are probability weighted sums. This suggests that the techniques for simple random variables may be extended to obtain approximations to the basic integrals for absolutely continuous random variables. Even when distributions are described analytically (e.g., normal, gamma, or beta distributions), these are usually convenient approximations to the actual distribution encountered in nature. Great precision in calculations may not be justified, except perhaps when small differences of large quantities or ratios of small quantities are involved.

A serious limitation to the approach in this chapter is the matrix size and memory requirements, which make it infeasible for student versions of MATLAB and for personal computers with insufficient memory. When these limitations do not prevent computations, there is considerable advantage in the formulation of problems involving unusual functions. This is particularly the case in dealing with conditional expectation and the regression problem.

We first consider the case of a single, bounded random variable X with density function f_X. The domain of f_X is the range of X, which we assume to be included in a bounded interval $[a, b]$. The approximating simple random variable Y takes on values $t_1, t_2, \cdots, t_n$ in the interval. We assume these are equally spaced, with constant increment $d = t_{i+1} - t_i = (b - a)/n$. We take each t_i to be the midpoint of the ith interval. Then $t_1 = a + d/2$ and $t_n = b - d/2$, with the others equally spaced. We have

$$E[g(X)] \approx E[g(Y)] = \sum_{i=1}^{n} g(t_i)P(Y = t_i)$$

Now $P(Y = t_i)$ is the probability that X takes on values in the ith subinterval. This is

$$P(Y = t_i) = P(t_i \leq X \leq t_{i+1}) = \int_{t_i}^{t_{i+1}} f_X(t) \, dt \approx f_X(t_i)d$$

For d small enough that f_X is essentially constant over each subinterval, the approximation $P(Y = t_i) = f_X(t_i)d$ is usually quite satisfactory for practical problems. We use this as the basis for calculating probabilities and expectations for bounded random variables. In the unbounded case, the density must go to zero fast enough that the probability beyond a certain point is negligible. If we can work with an interval large enough to contain essentially all of the probability mass, we can use the simple approximation. This is the same strategy used in approximating discrete, unbounded distributions, such as the Poisson or geometric, by a finite number of values. The following pair of procedures sets up the approximating values and probabilities.

———————————————— MATLAB Script ————————————————

```
% file tappr.m
% Sets up discrete approximation to distribution for X
% Version of 4/16/94
r = input('Enter matrix [a b] of x-range endpoints  ');
n = input('Enter number of x approximation points ');
d = (r(2) - r(1))/n;
t = (r(1):d:r(2)-d) +d/2;
PX = input('Enter density as a function of t ');
PX = PX*d;
PX = PX/sum(PX);
X  = t;
disp('Use row matrices X and PX as in the simple case')
```

For many of the standard distributions, it is probably better to use an analytical approach. The following nonstandard density function may serve as a useful illustration. The desired probabilities and expectations can be calculated by elementary means, which gives a check on the accuracy of the method.

EXAMPLE 6.1
Radial Tire Mileage

The life (in miles) of a certain brand of radial tires may be represented by a random variable X with density

$$f_X(t) = \begin{cases} t^2/a^3 & \text{for } 0 \leq t < a \\ (b/a)e^{-k(t-a)} & \text{for } a \leq t \end{cases}$$

where $a = 40{,}000$, $b = 20/3$, and $k = 1/4000$. Determine $P(X \geq 45{,}000)$, $E[X]$, and $\text{Var}[X]$.

_____ MATLAB Script _____

```
>> a = 40000;
>> b = 20/3;
>> k = 1/4000;
>> tappr
Enter matrix [a b] of x-range endpoints  [0 80000]
Enter number of x approximation points  80000/20
Enter density as a function of t  (t.^2/a^3).*(t < 40000) + ...
(b/a)*exp(k*(a-t)).*(t >= 40000)
Use row matrices X and PX as in the simple case
>> P = (X >= 45000)*PX'
P   =   0.1910
>> EX = X*PX'
EX  =   3.9332e+04
>> EX2 = X.^2*PX'
EX2 =   1.6212e+09
>> VX = EX2 - EX^2
VX  =   7.4164e+07
>> SX = sqrt(VX)
SX  =   8.6118e+03
```

In this case, we use an increment yielding a rather large number of approximation points. As a consequence, the results are quite accurate. A large number of approximating points in the single-variable case usually causes no memory problem.

2. JOINTLY DISTRIBUTED PAIR

For a pair $\{X, Y\}$ with joint density f_{XY}, we utilize the techniques developed for a pair of simple random variables. If we have n approximation values t_i

for X and m approximating values u_j for Y, we then have $n \cdot m$ pairs (t_i, u_j) corresponding to points on the plane. If we subdivide the horizontal axis for values of X with constant increments dx, as in the single-variable case, and the vertical axis for values of Y with constant increments dy, we have a grid structure consisting of rectangles of size $dx \times dy$. We select t_i and u_j at the midpoint of its increment, so that the point (t_i, u_j) is at the midpoint of the rectangle. If we let the approximating pair be $\{X^*, Y^*\}$, we assign

$$
\begin{aligned}
p_{ij} &= P((X^*, Y^*) = (t_i, u_j)) = P(X^* = t_i, Y^* = u_j) \\
&= P((X, Y) \in ij\text{th rectangle})
\end{aligned}
$$

As in the one-variable case, if the increments are small enough,

$$
P((X, Y) \in ij\text{th rectangle}) \approx dx \cdot dy \cdot f_{XY}(t, u_j)
$$

Because of the approximations involved, the sum of the p_{ij} may not be one. It is usually better in such a case to "standardize" or rationalize the total to one by dividing each p_{ij} by the sum. The following procedure sets up the P, t, and u matrices for calculating with the simple approximating pair. Calculations are then carried out in the usual manner for a joint simple pair.

—————————————————— MATLAB Script ——————————————————

```
% file tuappr.m
% Sets up discrete approximations to X, Y, t, u, and density
% Version of 10/31/93
rx = input('Enter matrix [a b] of X-range endpoints ');
ry = input('Enter matrix [c d] of Y-range endpoints ');
nx = input('Enter number of X approximation points ');
ny = input('Enter number of Y approximation points ');
dx = (rx(2) - rx(1))/nx;
dy = (ry(2) - ry(1))/ny;
X  = (rx(1):dx:rx(2)-dx) + dx/2;
Y  = (ry(1):dy:ry(2)-dy) + dy/2;
t  = ones(ny,1)*X;
u  = rot90(Y)*ones(1,nx);
P  = input('Enter expression for joint density ');
P  = dx*dy*P;
P  = P/sum(sum(P));
disp('Use array operations on X, Y, t, u, and P')
```

The first example is fairly simple to analyze by usual means, so that it provides a basis for comparison. We use rather large increments, giving only 20 approximation points for each variable. Note that this gives 400 joint approximation points!

EXAMPLE 6.2
Use of tuappr

Suppose $f_{XY}(t, u) = (8/9)tu$ for $1 \le t \le u \le 2$. This is the triangular region with vertices $(1, 1)$, $(2, 2)$, and $(1, 2)$. Straightforward calculations give $E[Y] = 232/135$ and

$$e(t) = E[Y \mid X = t] = \frac{2}{3} \cdot \frac{t^2 + 2t + 4}{t + 2} \qquad 1 \le t \le 2$$

Calculate approximations and compare.

Solution

_____ MATLAB Script _____

```
>> tuappr
Enter matrix [a b] of X-range endpoints  [1 2]
Enter matrix [c d] of Y-range endpoints  [1 2]
Enter number of X approximation points  20
Enter number of Y approximation points  20
Enter expression for joint density  (8/9)*t.*u.*(u >= t)
Use array operations on X, Y, t, u, and P
>> eY = sum(u.*P)./sum(P);      % Approximate E[Y|X=x]
>> e = (2/3)*(X.^2 + 2*X + 4)./(X + 2);  % Theoretical E[Y|X=x]
>> plot(X,eY)
>> hold on
>> plot(X,e,'-.')               % See Figure 6.1
---------                       % Commands for title, etc.
>> hold off
>> Q = u >= 3 - t;
>> G = (t+u).*Q + t.*u.*(1 - Q);
>> clear Q                      % To conserve memory
>> eZx = sum(G.*P)./sum(P);
>> clear G                      % To conserve memory
>> plot(X,eZx)                  % See Figure 6.2
---------                       % Commands for title, etc.
>> EY = sum(sum(u.*P))          % Approximate calculation of E[Y]
EY = 1.7125                     % Theoretical E[Y] = 232/135 = 1.7185
>> EY = eY*sum(P)'              % Alternate approximation
EY = 1.7125                     % For nx = ny = 100, value is 1.7174
```

EXAMPLE 6.3

The joint density $f_{XY}(t, u) = (1/28)(4t + 2u + 1)$ for $0 \le t \le 2$, $0 \le u \le 2$. Standard calculations give $E[X] = 25/21$, $\mathrm{Var}[X] = 131/441$, $E[Y] = 23/21$, and $\mathrm{Cov}[X, Y] = -8/441$. The regression line of Y on X is

$$u = -\frac{8}{131}t + \frac{3213}{2751}$$

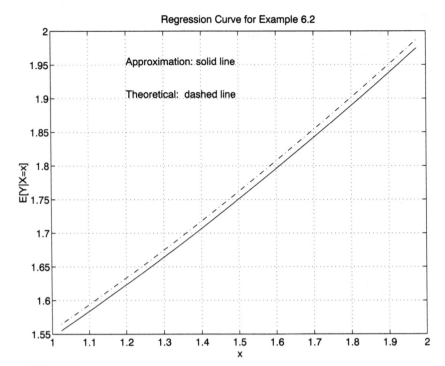

FIGURE 6.1

Also, the regression curve of Y on X is

$$u = e(t) = 1 + \frac{2}{12t + 9} \qquad 0 \le t \le 2$$

Determine approximations to these quantities and compare.

Solution

———————————— MATLAB Script ————————————

```
>> tuappr
Enter matrix [a b] of x-range endpoints   [0 2]
Enter matrix [c d] of y-range endpoints   [0 2]
Enter number of x approximation points   200
Enter number of y approximation points   200
Enter expression for joint density   (1/28)*(4*t + 2*u + 1)
Use array operations on X, Y, t, u, and P
>> EX = total(t.*P)              % function total(P) = sum(sum(P))
EX = 1.1905                      % Theoretical is 25/21 = 1.1905
>> EY = total(u.*P)
EY = 1.0952                      % Theoretical is 23/21 = 1.0952
>> EXY = total(t.*u.*P)
EXY = 1.2857                     % Theoretical is 9/7 = 1.2857
>> CV = EXY - EX*EY
```

Continues

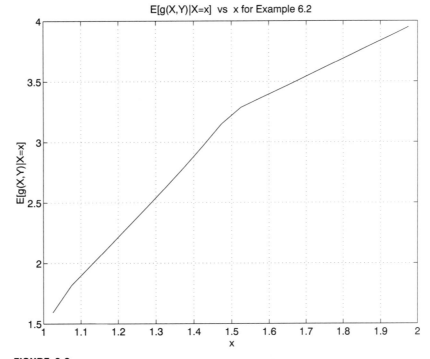

E[g(X,Y)|X=x] vs x for Example 6.2

FIGURE 6.2

```
CV = -0.0181                    % Theoretical is -8/441 = - 0.0181
>> EX2 = total(t.^2.*P)
EX2 = 1.7143
>> VX = EX2 - EX^2
VX =  0.2970                    % Theoretical is 131/441 = 0.2971
>> a = CV/VX
a  = -0.0611                    % Theoretical is -8/131 = - 0.0611
>> b = EY - a*EX
b  =  1.1679                    % Theoretical is 3213/2751 = 1.1679
>> eY = sum(u.*P)./sum(P);      % Approximate
>> e = 1 + 2./(12*X + 9);       % Theoretical
>> plot(X,e)
>> hold on
>> plot(X,eY,'.')               % See Figure 6.3
>> hold off                     % Commands for title, etc.
>> title('Theoretical (---)  and  Approximate (. . . .) E[Y|X = x]')
>> xlabel('x')
>> ylabel('E[Y|X=x]')
```

We next consider an example which is designed to show the use of indicator functions in the handling of densities with irregular areas and functions with composite definitions. The analytic solution is tedious and in-

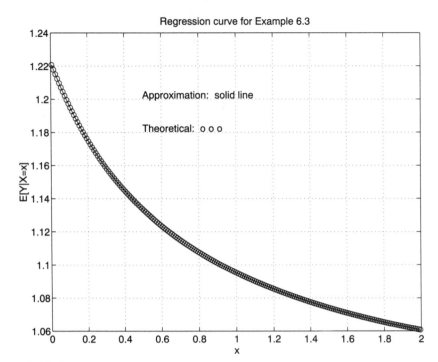

Regression curve for Example 6.3

FIGURE 6.3

volves several parts. By contrast, it is fairly easy to enter the data and obtain the MATLAB solution. Additionally, the graphics are obtained with minimal effort.

EXAMPLE 6.4
Function with Composite Definition

The joint density $f_{XY}(t, u) = (1/2)tu$ on the square with vertices $(1, 0)$, $(2, 1)$, $(1, 2)$, and $(0, 1)$. Consider the function

$$Z = g(X, Y) = \begin{cases} X & \text{for } X + Y \leq 2 \\ X^2 Y & \text{for } X + Y > 2 \end{cases}$$

The calculation of $E[Z|X = t]$ is somewhat tedious, and the result requires different expressions in each of four intervals.

$$E[Z \mid X = t] = \begin{cases} t & \text{for } 0 \leq t \leq 1/2 \\ (9 - 20t + 30t^2 - 6t^3 + 4t^4)/12 & \text{for } 1/2 < t \leq 1 \\ (9t + 32t^2 - 30t^3 + 6t^4)/12(2 - t) & \text{for } 1 < t \leq 3/2 \\ (14t^2 - 15t^3 + 6t^4 - t^5)/3(2 - t) & \text{for } 3/2 < t < 2 \end{cases}$$

Calculate the approximation and compare with the theoretical.

—————————————————————————— MATLAB Script ——————————————

```
>> tuappr
Enter matrix [a b] of x-range endpoints  [0 2]
Enter matrix [c d] of y-range endpoints  [0 2]
Enter number of x approximation points  50
Enter number of y approximation points  50
Enter expression for joint density  (1/2)*t.*u.*(u<=3-t)&(u<=1+t)&(u>=1
 -t)&(u>=t-1)
Use array operations on X, Y, t, u, and P
>> G = t.*(t + u <= 2) + (t.^2).*u.*(t + u > 2);
>> eZ = sum(G.*P)./sum(P);
>> clear G
>> A = X <= 0.5;
>> B = (X > 0.5)&(X <= 1);
>> C = (X > 1)&(X <= 1.5);
>> D = X > 1.5;
>> G1 = A.*X;
>> G2 = B.*(9 - 20*X + 30*X.^2 - 6*X.^3 + 4*X.^4)/12;
>> G3 = C.*((9*X + 32*X.^2 - 30*X.^3 + 6*X.^4)./(12*(2 -X)));
>> G4 = D.*((14*X.^2 - 15*X.^3 + 6*X.^4 - X.^5)./(3*(2 - X)));
>> e = G1 + G2 + G3 + G4;
>> plot(X,eZ)              % See Figure 6.4
>> hold on
>> plot(X,e,'o')
>> hold off               % Commands for title, etc.
```

——●

In each example considered, we find very good agreement between the theoretical regression curve and the approximation curve, suggesting the usefulness of the approach. In the last example, although given the theoretical result, it is easier to enter the data and make the approximate calculation than merely to enter the theoretical result. And considerable effort is required to obtain the theoretical result. Yet the approximation agrees with the theoretical result well enough for all practical purposes.

The principal limitation of the method is the size of the matrices needed for some problems. The memory requirements may well exceed the capacity of most personal computers. And the matrix size often exceeds the maximum size allowed in the student versions of MATLAB. For many cases, it may be desirable to utilize a program such as MAPLE to evaluate the double integrals. MATLAB has a toolbox which incorporates MAPLE into the system. We do not use this approach, since the current approach serves to give important insight into the nature of the probability calculations and provides an efficient approach to many commonly encountered problems.

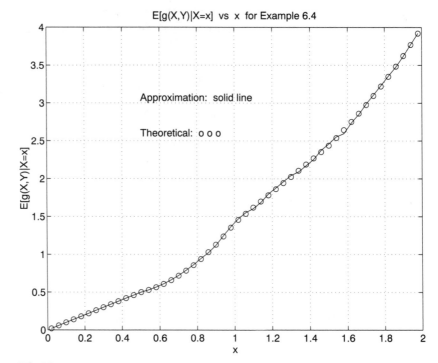

FIGURE 6.4

As in the case of joint simple random variables, we find it useful to incorporate the basic calculations into a single procedure, so that they can be be used after the problem has been set up in discrete form by tuappr.

_____ MATLAB Script _____

```
% file japprox.m
% Calculates basic quantities for X,Y
% Version of 12/14/93
% Assumes tuappr has set t, u, P
EX  = sum(sum(t.*P))       % E[X]
EY  = sum(sum(u.*P))       % E[Y]
EX2 = sum(sum((t.^2).*P))  % E[X^2]
EY2 = sum(sum((u.^2).*P))  % E[Y^2]
EXY = sum(sum(t.*u.*P))    % E[XY]
VX  = EX2 - EX^2           % Var[X]
VY  = EY2' - EY^2          % Var[Y]
cv = EXY - EX*EY;          % Cov[X,Y] = E[XY] - E[X]E[Y]
if abs(cv) > 1e-9          % to prevent roundoff error masking zero
   CV = cv
 else
   CV = 0
end
```

Continues

```
disp('Regression line of Y on X is u = at + b')
a = CV/VX                    % regression line of Y on X is
b = EY - a*EX                % u = at + b
R = CV/sqrt(VX*VY);          % correlation coefficient rho
disp(['The regression line of Y on X is:  u = ',num2str(a),'t
+ ',num2str(b),])
disp(['The correlation coefficient is:  rho = ',num2str(R),])
disp(' ')
eY = sum(u.*P)./sum(P);      % eY(t) = E[Y|X = t]
RL = a*X + b;
plot(X,RL)
hold on
plot(X,eY,'+')
hold off
grid
title('Regression line (----) and Regression curve (+ + + +)')
xlabel('X values')
ylabel('Y values')
clear eY                     % To conserve memory
clear RL
disp('Use array operations on X, Y, t, u, and P')
```

EXAMPLE 6.5
Use of japprox

Consider $\{X, Y\}$ with joint density function $f_{XY}(t, u) = \frac{6}{5}(t + 2u)$ on the triangular region bounded by $t = 0$, $u = 1$, and $u = t$. Calculate basic quantities for the pair.

Solution

_____ MATLAB Script _____

```
>> tuappr
Enter matrix [a b] of X-range endpoints   [0 1]
Enter matrix [c d] of Y-range endpoints   [0 1]
Enter number of X approximation points   100
Enter number of Y approximation points   100
Enter expression for joint density  (6/5)*(t+2*u).*(u>=t)
Use array operations on X, Y, t, u, and P
>> japprox
EX  =  0.4024      % Theoretical = 4/10   = 0.4000
EY  =  0.7492      % Theoretical = 3/4    = 0.7500
EX2 =  0.2225      % Theoretical = 11/50  = 0.2200
EY2 =  0.5991      % Theoretical = 3/5    = 0.6000
EXY =  0.3216      % Theoretical = 8/25   = 0.3200
VX  =  0.0606      % Theoretical = 3/50   = 0.0600
VY  =  0.0377      % Theoretical = 3/80   = 0.0375
CV  =  0.0201      % Theoretical = 2/100  = 0.0200
a   =  0.3320      % Theoretical = 1/3    = 0.3333
b   =  0.6156      % Theoretical = 37/60  = 0.6167
```

Continues

```
The regression line of Y on X is:   u = 0.332t + 0.6156
The correlation coefficient is:   rho = 0.4208     % Theoretical
= (4/30)sqrt(10)
Use array operations on X, Y, t, u, and P        % = 0.4216
>> print         % See Figure 6.5
```

The procedure tappr in the single-variable case and tuappr in the two-variable case enable us to set up simple approximations to the distributions for absolutely continuous random variables. Once an approximation is formed, calculations proceed essentially as in the simple case. In the two-variable case, a procedure japprox performs the same calculations as jsimple. Because of the comparatively large number of value points for such quantities as the conditional expectation (regression curve), however, it is usually better to display the results graphically than in tabular form.

The principal limitation of the approach is the "size" of the problems, in terms of matrix size and memory requirements. This puts limits on the use of student versions of MATLAB and may exceed the available memory of many personal computers. But there are no inherent limitations in the approach, and satisfactory results are usually obtained with moderate numbers of approximating values.

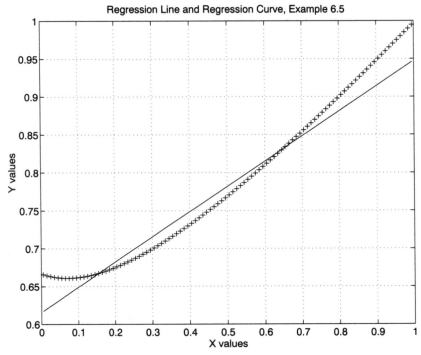

FIGURE 6.5

REINFORCEMENT EXERCISES AND EXLORATION PROBLEMS

REINFORCEMENT EXERCISES

P6.1 The pair $\{X, Y\}$ has the following joint density function f_{XY} on the square $0 \le t \le 1$, $0 \le u \le 1$:

$$f_{XY}(t, u) = \begin{cases} 4tu & \text{for } u \ge t \quad (0 \le t \le u \le 1) \\ t + u & \text{for } u \le t \quad (0 \le u < t \le 1) \end{cases}$$

$$E[X] = \frac{77}{120} \qquad E[Y] = \frac{73}{120} \qquad E[X^2] = \frac{7}{15} \qquad E[XY] = \frac{7}{18}$$

$$E[Y \mid X = t] = \frac{8 + 5t^2 - 8t^3}{3(4 + 3t - 4t^2)} \qquad 0 \le t \le 1$$

Use the approximation procedures to calculate these quantities and compare with the theoretical.

Suggestion: Draw a figure showing the regions.

P6.2 The pair $\{X, Y\}$ has joint density function $f_{XY}(t, u) = \frac{2}{5}(t + 2u)$ on the region bounded by $t = 0$, $u = 0$, $u = 1$, and $u = 2 - t$. Calculations show

$$E[X] = 13/15, \qquad E[Y] = 31/60, \qquad E[X^2] = 29/30, \qquad E[XY] = 29/75, \quad \text{and}$$

$$E[Y \mid X = t] = \begin{cases} (3t + 4)/6(t + 1) & \text{for } 0 \le t \le 1 \\ (16 - 10t + t^2)/12 & \text{for } 1 \le t \le 2 \end{cases}$$

Use the approximation procedures to determine these quantities and compare.

Suggestion: Draw a sketch of the region

P6.3 The pair $\{X, Y\}$ has joint density function $f_{XY}(t, u) = \frac{2}{3}(t + 3u^2)$ on the square $0 \le t \le 1$ and $0 \le u \le 1$

    a. Use the approximation procedures to approximate the regression line and the regression curve of Y on X.

    b. Let

$$W = \begin{cases} 2XY & \text{for } Y \le 2X \\ Y & \text{for } Y > 2X \end{cases}$$

Plot the discrete approximation to the graph for

$$u = E[W \mid X = t]$$

Suggestion: Draw a figure and identify appropriate regions.

P6.4 Use tuappr to set up the joint density $f_{XY}(t, u) = (8/9)tu$ for $1 \le t \le u \le 2$.

    a. Call for japprox and note the results (including a plot of the regression curve).

b. Then call for jsimple and input P, X, and Y. Note the results. Plot the regression curve (eY vs. X).

Compare the results. Are there any surprises? Compare the procedures jsimple and japprox. How do they differ? Why?

Random Sums

PREVIEW

We consider some important special cases of sums of a random number of independent, identically distributed (iid) random variables. After establishing a model for such a random sum and determining a generating function and a moment generating function, we consider useful Matlab implementations. These are utilized in several important applications, including random demand, Poisson decomposition, extreme values of a random number of random variables, and Bernoulli trials with random execution times or costs.

1. A RANDOM NUMBER OF RANDOM VARIABLES

A variety of important problems in probability require the treatment of a random number of random variables selected from a given class. We treat a special case of summing a random number of iid random variables, with the counting random variable independent of the terms summed. For a more complete treatment of the underlying theory, utilizing conditional expectation, see *PA*, Chapters 20 and 21.

Some standard examples include:

1. Total purchase by a random number of customers.
2. Total service time for a random number of units.
3. Net gain in a random number of plays of a game.
4. Extreme values of a random number of random quantities.

A USEFUL MODEL: COMPOUND DEMAND

To formulate the model we consider:

1. *Two related sequences:*

    Basic sequence: $\quad \{X_n: 0 \le n\}$

    Incremental sequence: $\quad \{Y_n: 0 \le n\}$

    These are related as follows:

    $$X_n = \sum_{k=0}^{n} Y_k \quad \text{for } n \ge 0, \; X_n = 0 \quad \text{for } n < 0$$

    $$\text{and} \quad Y_n = X_n - X_{n-1} \quad \text{for all } n$$

2. *A counting random variable N,* which determines the number of incremental random variables to be summed. The sum itself is a random variable.

    $$D = X_N = \sum_{n=0}^{\infty} I_{\{N=n\}} X_n = \sum_{k=0}^{N} Y_k$$

    Random variable D has the property

    $$D(\omega) = X_n(\omega) = \sum_{k=0}^{n} Y_k(\omega) \quad \text{whenever } N(\omega) = n$$

We use the demand of a random number of customers as a basic interpretive model and call D the *compound demand*. Unless we specify otherwise in a particular case, we make the following assumptions, which we refer to as the *usual assumptions:*

1. $Y_0 = X_0 = 0$.
2. $\{Y_k: 1 \le k\}$ is iid (independent, identically distributed).
3. $\{N, Y_k: 1 \le k\}$ is independent.

We use the generating function g_X for nonnegative integer random variables and the moment generating function $M_X(s)$ in the general case.

$$g_X(s) = E[s^X] = \sum_k p_k s^k, \quad \text{where } p_k = P(X = k)$$

$$\text{and} \quad M_X(s) = E[e^{sX}]$$

Under the usual assumptions:

1. The Y_k have the common distribution function F_Y and common moment generating function M_Y.
2. If the Y_k are nonnegative, integer valued, they have the common generating function g_Y.

When $\{Y_k : 1 \le k\}$ is iid, we have $M_{X_n}(s) = M_Y^n(s)$ and $g_{X_n}(s) = g_Y^n(s)$. Although these assumptions are somewhat restrictive, they make possible a precise analysis which can serve as a guide even in cases for which the model is a rather crude approximation. In the analysis, we utilize the facts that $E[I_A] = P(A)$ and, under very general conditions on the random variables,

$$E\left[\sum_{k=0}^{\infty} X_k\right] = \sum_{k=0}^{\infty} E[X_k]$$

THE POISSON COUNTING PROCESS

We frequently assume the counting random variable N has a Poisson distribution. Very often this is because the quantity counted is the number of occurrences in a given time interval of a phenomenon which is separated by independent, identically distributed, exponential waiting times. Such counting random variables are encountered frequently in reliability theory. Suppose a device has time to failure which is a random variable with exponential distribution. Immediately upon failure, it is replaced by a similar unit. Failure times for successive units are independent. The time to failure S_n for n units is thus the sum of n independent, identically distributed exponential random variables. Suppose for any time $t > 0$ the number of failures in the interval $(0, t]$ is a random quantity N_t. The following analysis shows that N_t has a Poisson distribution for any $t > 0$.

Let X_i be the life duration of the ith unit. The first unit is installed at time $t = 0$. Let S_n be the time of failure of the nth unit, and let N_t be the number of failures up to and including time t.

If $X_i \sim$ exponential (λ), then $S_n \sim$ gamma (n, λ)

The count in the interval $(0, t]$ is at least n iff the nth failure occurs no later than time t. Hence,

$$P(N_t \ge n) = P(S_n \le t)$$

A fundamental relationship between the gamma distribution and the Poisson distribution, noted in Chapter 3, ensures that the random variable $N_t \sim$ Poisson (λt).

This pattern is observed to hold, at least approximately, in a variety of natural phenomena. The times of failure are referred to generically as *arrival times* and the times between failures are called the *waiting times* or *interarrival times*. The class of random variables N_t for all parameter values $t > 0$ constitutes the *Poisson process,* which has many important properties that make it mathematically tractable.

EXAMPLE 7.1

A Service Facility

A service facility takes jobs of a certain type in succession. The time in hours to complete the ith job is a random quantity $Y_i \sim$ exponential ($\lambda = 2$), so that the average job time is $1/\lambda = 1/2$ hour. The service facility is kept busy, and completion times for successive jobs are independent. For each value $10 \le k \le 20$, what is the probability of completing k or more jobs in an eight hour workday?

─────────────────── MATLAB Script ───────────────────

```
>> k = 10:20;
>> m = 2*8;
>> P = cpoisson(m,k);
>> disp([k;P]')
   10.0000    0.9567
   11.0000    0.9226
   12.0000    0.8730
   13.0000    0.8069
   14.0000    0.7255
   15.0000    0.6325
   16.0000    0.5333
   17.0000    0.4340
   18.0000    0.3407
   19.0000    0.2577
   20.0000    0.1878
```

2. THE GENERATING FUNCTION AND MOMENT GENERATING FUNCTION

Under the usual assumptions on the compound demand D, we have the following important formulas:

Transforms for the compound demand

$$M_D(s) = g_N[M_Y(s)] \quad \text{and}$$
$$g_D(s) = g_N[g_Y(s)] \quad \text{for integer-valued } Y_i$$

These expressions for the moment generating function and the generating function provide a key element in much of the analysis of this chapter. A derivation is found in Section 4, the appendix to this chapter.

Often, it may suffice to know the expectation, and perhaps the variance, of the compound demand. Again, under the usual assumptions:

Expectation and variance for the compound demand

$$E[D] = E[N]E[Y] \quad \text{and}$$
$$\text{Var}[D] = E[N]\text{Var}[Y] + \text{Var}[N]E[Y]^2$$

A derivation is provided in Section 4.

EXAMPLE 7.2
A Compound
Demand

The number of customers in a major appliance store is equally likely to be 1, 2, or 3. Each customer buys 0, 1, or 2 items with respective probabilities 0.5, 0.4, and 0.1. Customers buy independently, regardless of the number of customers.

    a. What is the expected number sold?
    b. What is the probability that three or more are sold?

Solution

$E[N] = 2$ and $E[Y] = 0.6$, so that $E[D] = 1.2$. For the distribution, we utilize g_D.

$$g_N(s) = \frac{1}{3}(s + s^2 + s^3) \quad \text{and} \quad g_Y(s) = \frac{1}{10}(5 + 4s + s^2)$$

$$g_D(s) = g_N[g_Y(s)] = \frac{1}{3}(g_Y(s) + g_Y(s)^2 + g_Y(s)^3)$$

Raising the polynomial $g_Y(s)$ to second and third powers and adding, we get

$$g_D(s) = \frac{1}{3000}(875 + 1100s + 675s^2 + 264s^3 + 73s^4 + 12s^5 + s^6)$$

$$= 0.2917 + 0.3667s + 0.2250s^2 + 0.0880s^3$$
$$+ 0.0243s^4 + 0.0040s^5 + 0.0003s^6$$

$$P(D \geq 3) = 0.0880 + 0.0243 + 0.0040 + 0.0003 = 0.1166.$$

In the case of simple N and Y_i, we have two MATLAB programs which perform the necessary calculations to determine the distribution for composite demand D, provided the maximum value of N and the number of values of Y are not too great.

MATLAB IMPLEMENTATION: THE PROCEDURE genD

If the Y_i are nonnegative, integer-valued, then so is D, and there is a generating function. Before writing a MATLAB procedure, we examine a strategy for computation. Suppose

$$g_N(s) = p_0 + p_1 s + p_2 s^2 + \cdots + p_n s^n$$
$$g_Y(s) = \pi_0 + \pi_1 s + \pi_2 s^2 + \cdots + \pi_m s^m$$

We enter the coefficients of g_N and g_Y and calculate the coefficients for powers of g_Y:

$pN = [p_0 p_1 \cdots p_n]$	$1 \times (n + 1)$	Coefficients of g_N
$y = [\pi_0 \pi_1 \cdots \pi_m]$	$1 \times (m + 1)$	Coefficients of g_Y
$\cdots$		
$y2 = \text{conv}(y, y)$	$1 \times (2m + 1)$	Coefficients of g_Y^2
$y3 = \text{conv}(y, y2)$	$1 \times (3m + 1)$	Coefficients of g_Y^3
$\cdots$		
$yn = \text{conv}(y, y(n - 1))$	$1 \times (nm + 1)$	Coefficients of g_Y^n

We wish to generate a matrix Y whose rows contain the coefficients for the successive powers of g_Y. To do this, we must augment each yi with sufficient zeros to make the common length $nm + 1$, the length of yn. We achieve this as follows:

Set

$$Y(1,:) = [1 \text{ zeros}(n * m)];$$

Then $\text{conv}(y, Y(1,:))$ is $y1$ with extra zeros.

Set $Y(2,:) =$ first $nm + 1$ elements of $\text{conv}(y, Y(1,:))$

Set $Y(3,:) =$ first $nm + 1$ elements of $\text{conv}(y, Y(2,:))$

- - - - -

Continue in this fashion to get $Y(4,:), \cdots, Y(n,:) = yn$.

Calculate the matrix of coefficients of g_D: $pD = pN * Y$.

The following procedure implements this strategy:

—————————————————— MATLAB Script ——————————————————

```
% file genD.m
% Procedure for calculating generating function for D
% Version of 5/24/93
disp('Do not forget zero coefficients for missing powers ')
pN = input('Enter probabilities for N ');
y  = input('Enter probabilities for Y ');
n  = length(pN) - 1;
m  = length(y)  - 1;
Y  = zeros(n + 1,n*m + 1);      % Base for generating Y
Y(1,:) = [1 zeros(1,n*m)];      % [1] augmented to 1x(n*m + 1)
for i = 1:n                     % Step by step buildup of rows of Y
    a = conv(y,Y(i,:));         % Convolution adds extra zeros:
1x(n*m + 1 + m)
    Y(i+1,:) = a(1:(n*m + 1));  % Removal of extra zeros: 1x(n*m + 1)
end
pD = pN*Y;
k  = 0:n*m;                     % Display details
gD = [k; pD]';
disp('Values of D are in row matrix k; probabilities are in pD.')
disp('To view the distribution, call for gD.')
```

●————

EXAMPLE 7.3
MATLAB Solution of Example 7.2   We utilize genD to solve Example 7.2. First, we determine the matrices representing g_N and g_Y. The coefficients are the probabilities that each integer value is observed. Note that the *zero coefficients for any missing powers* must be included.

$$pN = \frac{1}{3}[0 \ 1 \ 1 \ 1] \quad \text{and} \quad pY = \frac{1}{10}[5 \ 4 \ 1]$$

```
>> genD
 Do not forget zero coefficients for missing powers
 Enter probabilities for N (1/3)*[0 1 1 1]
 Enter probabilities for Y 0.1*[5 4 1]
 Values of D are in row matrix k; probabilities are in pD.
 To view the distribution, call for gD.
>> disp(gD)              % Optional call for display
            0      0.2917
       1.0000      0.3667
       2.0000      0.2250
       3.0000      0.0880
       4.0000      0.0243
       5.0000      0.0040
       6.0000      0.0003
>> ED = k*pD'
ED   = 1.2000
>> P3 = (k >= 3)*pD'
P3   = 0.1167
```

The following is a straightforward numerical example.

EXAMPLE 7.4
A Numerical Example

$$g_N(s) = \frac{1}{5}(1 + s + s^2 + s^3 + s^4) \qquad g_Y(s) = 0.1(5s + 3s^2 + 2s^3)$$

Solution

————————————— MATLAB Script —————————————

```
>> pN = 0.2*[1 1 1 1 1];
>> pY = 0.1*[0 5 3 2];
>> genD
Do not forget zero coefficients for missing powers
Enter probabilities for N pN
Enter probabilities for Y pY
Values of D are in row matrix k; probabilities are in pD.
To view the distribution, call for gD.
>> disp(gD)                    % Optional viewing of complete distribution
            0      0.2000
       1.0000      0.1000
       2.0000      0.1100
       3.0000      0.1250
       4.0000      0.1155
       5.0000      0.1110
       6.0000      0.0964
```

Continues

```
     7.0000      0.0696
     8.0000      0.0424
     9.0000      0.0203
    10.0000      0.0075
    11.0000      0.0019
    12.0000      0.0003
>>N = k == 3;
>> p3 = (k == 3)*pD'              % P(D=3)
P3 =   0.1250
>> P4_12 = ((k >= 4)&(k <= 12))*pD'
P4_12 = 0.4650                    % P(4 <= D <= 12)
```

The procedure genD is limited to simple N and Y_i, with nonnegative integer values. Sometimes, as shown in the Example 4.7 on the optimal stocking of merchandise, a random variable with unbounded range may be approximated by a simple random variable. The solution in the following example utilizes the same approximation procedure for the counting random variable N.

EXAMPLE 7.5
Approximation to Poisson N

Suppose the number of customers is represented by $N \sim$ Poisson (8). The demand of each customer takes on values 0, 1, or 2 with respective probabilities 1/4, 1/2, and 1/4. Under the usual independence assumptions, approximate the distribution for D with enough terms to include essentially all of the probability, and then determine $P(D \le 4)$.

Solution

──────────────────────── MATLAB Script ────────────────────────

```
>> cpoisson(8,[10 15 20 25 30])    % Check for sufficient terms
ans =
    0.2834    0.0173    0.0003    0.0000    0.0000    % Use 25
>> pN = [ipoisson(8,0:24) cpoisson(8,25)];
>> pY = 0.25*[1 2 1];
>> genD
 Do not forget zero coefficients for missing powers
Enter probabilities for N pN
Enter probabilities for Y pY
Values of D are in row matrix k; probabilities are in pD.
To view the distribution, call for gD.
>> disp(gD)
         0      0.0025
    1.0000      0.0099
    2.0000      0.0248
    3.0000      0.0463
    4.0000      0.0711
    5.0000      0.0939
```

Continues

```
    6.0000      0.1099
    7.0000      0.1165
    8.0000      0.1132
    9.0000      0.1021
   10.0000      0.0861   % Calculated table extends to k =50
   .......      ......   % Result truncated to save space
>> sum(pD)               % Check on sufficiency of approximation
ans =   1.0000           % - applied to entire calculated table
>> P4 = (k <= 4)*pD'     % P(D <= 4) = sum of first five coefficients
P4   =   0.1545
```

The next simple example shows a fundamental limitation of the genD procedure. The values are not limited to integers, and there are large gaps in the
values of the random variables.

EXAMPLE 7.6
Noninteger Values

A service shop has three standard charges for a certain class of warranty
services it performs: $10, $12.50, and $15. The number of jobs received in
a normal workday can be considered a random variable N which takes on
values 0, 1, 2, 3, or 4 with equal probabilities of 0.2. The job types for arrivals
may be represented by an iid class $\{Y_i: 1 \leq i \leq 4\}$, independent of the arrival
process. The Y_i take on values 10, 12.5, or 15 with respective probabilities
0.5, 0.3, and 0.2. Let C be the total amount of services rendered in a day.
Determine the distribution for C.

This example illustrates the need for the moment generating function M_D.

MATLAB IMPLEMENTATION: THE PROCEDURE mgD

Suppose $X = \sum_{i=1}^{n} t_i I_{A_i}$ in canonical form. That is, A_i is the event $\{X = t_i\}$ for
each of the distinct values in the range of X, with $p_i = P(A_i) = P(X = t_i)$.
Then the moment generating function for X is

$$M_X(s) = \sum_{i=1}^{n} p_i e^{st_i}$$

To determine M_X, we simply require the distribution for X. If $\{X, Y\}$ is an
independent pair, then the moment generating function for the sum $X + Y$
is the product of the moment generating functions. We need powers of the
moment generating function for Y in $M_D(s)$. Now if $Y = \sum_{j=1}^{m} u_j I_{B_j}$, with
$P(Y = u_j) = \pi_j$, we have

$$M_X(s)M_Y(s) = \left(\sum_{i=1}^{n} p_i e^{st_i}\right)\left(\sum_{j=1}^{m} \pi e^{su_j}\right) = \sum_{i,j} p_i \pi_j e^{s(t_i + u_j)}$$

The various values are sums $t_i + u_j$ of pairs (t_i, u_j) of values. Each of these sums has probability $p_i \pi_j$ for the values corresponding to t_i, u_j. Since more than one pair sum may have the same value, we need to sort the values, consolidate like values, and add the probabilities for like values to achieve the distribution for the sum. This may be done with the function csort. If we can produce the pair products for probabilities and the pair sums for values, we should be able to implement the computation of the distribution for the sum of independent random variables, corresponding to multiplying their moment generating functions. The following two auxiliary functions achieve these ends.

——————————— MATLAB Script ———————————

```
function y=pairsum(a,b)
% Version of 11/1/93
n = length(a);
m = length(b);
t = ones(m,1)*a;      % n rows of a
u = b'*ones(1,n);     % m columns of b
c = t + u;
y = c(:)';
```

——————————— MATLAB Script ———————————

```
function y=pairprod(a,b)
% Version of 11/1/93
n = length(a);
m = length(b);
t = ones(m,1)*a;      % n rows of a
u = b'*ones(1,n);     % m columns of b
c = t.*u;
y = c(:)';
```

The following procedure utilizes these functions and csort to implement the computation of the distribution for the compound demand.

——————————— MATLAB Script ———————————

```
% file mgD
% Moment generating function for D
% Version of 11/3/93
% Uses csort, pairsum, pairprod
g   = input('Enter probabilities for N  ');
y   = input('Enter values for Y  ');
p   = input('Enter probabilities Y  ');
n   = length(g);               % Initialization
```

Continues

```
a = 0;
b = 1;
D  = [0 g(1)]';
i = 1;
while i < n                         % Iterative computation
 a = pairsum(y,a);
 b = pairprod(p,b);
 D = [D [a;b*g(i+1)]];
 D = csort(D(1,:),D(2,:));
 i = i+1;
end
POS = D(2,:) > 1e-9;                % Removal of zero probability values
D = D(:,POS);
k = D(1,:);
pD = D(2,:);
D = D';
disp('Values of D are in row matrix k; probabilities are in pD')
disp('To view the distribution, call for D')
```

Remark: Note the difference in data for genD and the new procedure mgD. The data for N are treated the same in both cases, with zeros in the positions of missing integer values. But for Y in mgD, the actual values are put in a row matrix and the probabilities for these values are put in a corresponding row matrix. Even if Y is integer valued, there are no zeros in the probability matrix for missing values.

●
EXAMPLE 7.7
The Service Shop

———————————— MATLAB Script ——————————

```
>> pN = 0.2*[1 1 1 1 1];            % Enter data
>> y = [10 12.5 15];
>> pY = 0.1*[5 3 2];
>> mgD                              % Call for the procedure
Enter probabilities for N  pN
Enter values for Y  y
Enter probabilities Y  pY
Values of D are in row matrix k; probabilities are in pD
To view the distribution, call for D
>> disp(D)                          % Optional display
           0      0.2000
     10.0000      0.1000
     12.5000      0.0600
     15.0000      0.0400
     20.0000      0.0500
     22.5000      0.0600
     25.0000      0.0580
     27.5000      0.0240
```

Continues

30.0000	0.0330
32.5000	0.0450
35.0000	0.0570
37.5000	0.0414
40.0000	0.0353
42.5000	0.0372
45.0000	0.0486
47.5000	0.0468
50.0000	0.0352
52.5000	0.0187
55.0000	0.0075
57.5000	0.0019
60.0000	0.0003

We next recalculate the numerical Example 7.4, using mgD instead of genD. Note the difference in the data and its format.

EXAMPLE 7.8

Example 7.4
Revisited

_____ MATLAB Script _____

```
>> pN = 0.2*[1 1 1 1 1];
>> y = 1:3;
>> pY = 0.1*[5 3 2];
>> mgD
Enter probabilities for N   pN
Enter values for Y   y
Enter probabilities Y   pY
Values of D are in row matrix k; probabilities are in pD.
To view the distribution, call for D.
>> disp(D)
         0     0.2000
    1.0000     0.1000
    2.0000     0.1100
    3.0000     0.1250
    4.0000     0.1155
    5.0000     0.1110
    6.0000     0.0964
    7.0000     0.0696
    8.0000     0.0424
    9.0000     0.0203
   10.0000     0.0075
   11.0000     0.0019
   12.0000     0.0003
>> P3 = (k==3)*pD'
P3 =   0.1250
>> ED = k*pD'
```

Continues

```
>> M = ((k>=4)&(k<=12));
>> P4_12 = ((k>=4)&(k<=12))*pD'
P4_12 = 0.4650
ED =  3.4000
>> P7 = (k >= 7)*pD'
P7 = 0.1421
```

———●

As expected, the results are the same as those obtained with genD.

Limitation: The procedure mgD works very well for a small maximum value of N and not too many values of Y. However, it becomes rather memory and computation intensive as the size increases. Although there are no inherent limitations on size, memory limitations of the machine place practical limits. For example, an attempt was made to use mgD to solve Example 7.5 which uses the finite approximation to the Poisson distribution. After about ten minutes on a SPARCstation 1+, an "out of memory" signal appeared. The solution using genD takes less than two seconds on the same machine. For smaller numbers of values, the difference in time is negligible, and mgD handles a wider variety of problems.

3. SOME ADDITIONAL APPLICATIONS

THE POISSON DECOMPOSITION

When the counting random variable is Poisson, a random number of multino-mial trials yields a very important Poisson decomposition. First, we apply the generating function formula to the Bernoulli, or binomial, case.

Random number of Bernoulli trials If the counting random variable N is independent of the results of the trials and S is the number of successes, then

$$g_S(s) = g_N(q + ps) = g_N(1 + p(s - 1))$$

If $N \sim$ Poisson (μ), the number of successes $S \sim$ Poisson $(p\mu)$. To see this, note that $Y_k = I_{E_k}$, so that $g_Y(s) = q + ps = 1 - p + ps = 1 + p(s - 1)$. For $N \sim$ Poisson (μ),

$$g_S(s) = g_N[g_Y(s)] = e^{\mu(g_Y(s)-1)} = e^{\mu p(s-1)}$$

which shows that $S \sim$ Poisson $(p\mu)$.

●———————————————

EXAMPLE 7.9
Police Alarms

A police department receives alarms at a daily rate which can be modeled as $N \sim$ Poisson (1000). Only about ten percent of these are valid. What is the probability that the number of valid alarms is greater than or equal to 100? What is the probability of receiving 80 to 120 valid calls?

Solution On the basis of a Bernoulli trials model, the number N_a of authentic alarms is Poisson ($1000 \times 0.1 = 100$). Thus,

———————————— MATLAB Script ————————————

```
>> P100 = cpoisson(100,100)
P100 =   0.5133
>> P80_120 = cpoisson(100,80) - cpoisson(100,121)
P80_120 = 0.9599
```

EXAMPLE 7.10
Machine Tool
Bids

Bids are opened on a surplus machine tool. There are five potential bidders, with probability 0.6 that each will bid. The amounts they bid (in thousands of dollars) are iid uniform [70, 120]. What is the probability there will be at least one bid for 100 or more?

Solution The probability that any one bid is 100 or more is

$$(120 - 100)/(120 - 70) = 0.4$$

Thus, $pY = [0.6\ 0.4]$, and $pN = \text{ibinom}(5, 0.6, 0:5)$.

———————————— MATLAB Script ————————————

```
>> pY = [0.6 0.4];
>> pN = ibinom(5,0.6,0:5);
>> genD
Do not forget zero coefficients for missing powers
Enter probabilities for N pN
Enter probabilities for Y pY
Values of D are in row matrix k; probabilities are in pD.
To view the distribution, call for gD.
>> P = (k > 0)*pD'
P =   0.7464
```

An extension of the result for Poisson N to multinomial trials yields the:

Poisson decomposition Consider a random number of multinomial trials in which each outcome Y_i is one of m possible types (represented by integers $1 \leq k \leq m$), with probabilities $\{p_k : 1 \leq k \leq m\}$. If the counting random variable $N \sim$ Poisson (μ) is independent of the outcomes, and N_k is the number of outcomes of the kth type, then

1. $N_k \sim$ Poisson (μp_k) and
2. $\{N_k : 1 \leq k \leq m\}$ is an independent class.

The fact that each $N_k \sim$ Poisson (μp_k) is implied by the result on Bernoulli trials, since if we count the number of results of the kth type, we simply have a Bernoulli sequence, with success if the outcome is of kth type and failure otherwise. More detailed, but elementary, analysis using properties of ordinary multinomial trials (see the discussion in Chapter 3) is needed to establish the remarkable fact that the class is independent.

Remark: The Poisson decomposition and the fact that the sum of independent Poisson random variables is Poisson provide a significant computational advantage for many problems. The MATLAB programs ipoisson and cpoisson are valuable tools, since they make possible calculation of Poisson probabilities with unusual parameter values not found in tables.

EXAMPLE 7.11
Hobby Shop
Mailing

Managers of a hobby shop plan a mailing in which they make a special offer. The primary purpose, of course, is to increase their sales and customer base. But, they also hope that the response will provide a test of two possible mail-order markets. Potential customers receive a flier and a return card which allows them to order one of three very attractive items at an exceptional price. To identify the separate markets, the return cards are color coded. To estimate the stock they need, the managers make the following assumptions.

Blue mailing. The number N_B of returns is assumed to be Poisson (100). Each of the three items offered is equally likely to be selected.

Gold mailing. The number $N_G \sim$ Poisson (80). The respective probabilities for selecting each of the items is 0.4, 0.35, or 0.25.

What is the expected total number of each item (combined request in both mailings)? What is the probability the total request for Item 1 is at least 75?

Solution

The quantities N_{B1}, N_{B2}, and N_{B3} are each Poisson (100/3). The quantities N_{G1}, N_{G2}, and N_{G3} are Poisson with parameters 32, 28, and 20, respectively. Under the assumption that $\{N_B, N_G\}$ is an independent pair, the class $\{N_{B1}, N_{B2}, N_{B3}, N_{G1}, N_{G2}, N_{G3}\}$ is an independent class of Poisson random variables. The sum of any subset of these random variables must also be a Poisson random variable with parameter equal to the sum of the parameters for the individual variables in that subset. Thus,

$$E[N_{B1} + N_{G1}] = (100/3) + 32 = 65.3$$
$$E[N_{B2} + N_{G2}] = 61.3 \quad E[N_{B3} + N_{G3}] = 53.3$$

$N_1 = N_{B1} + N_{G1} \sim$ Poisson $((100/3) + 32)$. Use of cpoisson gives $P(N_1 \geq 75) = 0.1294$.

EXTREME VALUES OF A RANDOM NUMBER OF RANDOM VARIABLES

Consider an iid sequence $\{Y_i: 1 \leq i\}$ of nonnegative random variables and let N be a counting random variable independent of the Y sequence. For a fixed positive integer, let

$$V_n = \min\{Y_1, Y_2, \cdots, Y_n\} \quad \text{and} \quad W_n = \max\{Y_1, Y_2, \cdots, Y_n\}$$
$$\text{with } V_0 = W_0 = 0$$

Then

$$P(V_n > t) = P(Y > t)^n \quad \forall\, n \geq 1 \quad \text{with } P(V_0 > t) = 0 \quad \forall\, t \geq 0$$
$$P(W_n \leq t) = P(Y \leq t)^n \quad \text{with } P(W_0 \leq t) = 1 \quad \forall\, t \geq 0$$

We wish to determine the distribution for the maximum and minimum of a random number N of the Y_i. The following general result provides easy solutions in many cases.

For a class $\{N, Y_i: 1 \leq i\}$ as described above, let

$$V_N = \min\{Y_1, Y_2, \cdots, Y_N\} = \sum_{n=0}^{\infty} I_{\{N=n\}} V_n \quad \text{and}$$

$$W_N = \max\{Y_1, Y_2, \cdots, Y_N\} = \sum_{n=0}^{\infty} I_{\{N=n\}} W_n$$

Then

(a) $P(V_N > t) = g_N(P(Y > t)) - P(N = 0)$ for $t \geq 0$.
(b) $P(W_N \leq t) = g_N(P(Y \leq t))$ for $t \geq 0$.

A proof is provided in the Section 4.

EXAMPLE 7.12
Bids on Property

A property is put up for sale. The number of bids is represented by a counting random variable having values from 1 to 6 with respective probabilities 0.1, 0.2, 0.3, 0.2, 0.1, and 0.1. Suppose the bids in thousands of dollars are iid, with $Y_i = 100X_i$, where $X_i \sim \text{beta}(3, 2)$. Then $P(Y \leq t) = P(X \leq t/100)$. What is the probability of at least one bid of \$85,000 dollars or more?

Solution

We want the probability that the maximum W_N is at least \$85,000. According to the result above,

$$P(W > t) = 1 - g_N(P(Y \leq t)) = 1 - g_N(P(X \leq t/100))$$
$$\text{where } X \sim \text{beta}(5, 2)$$

```
>> pN = 0.1*[0 1 2 3 2 1 1];    % Coefficients in ascending order
>> gN = fliplr(pN);             % Coefficients in descending order
>> P85 = 1 - polyval(gN,betadbn(5,2,0.85))
P85 =   0.5385
>> t = 70:95;                   % Calculations for graph
>> P = 1 - polyval(gN,betadbn(5,2,t/100));
>> plot(t,P)
>> xlabel('Maximum Bid in Thousands of Dollars')
>> ylabel('Probability')
>> print                        % See Figure 7.1
```

In the case of seeking a minimum bid, we use the result for the minimum of a random number of random variables with *one important change*. The general result is determined with the understanding that the minimum value of zero random variables is zero. However, for bidding the receipt of zero bids does not provide a minimum bid. We must rule out the case $N = 0$, so that the general result is modified to

$$P(V_N \le t) = 1 - g_N(P(Y > t))$$

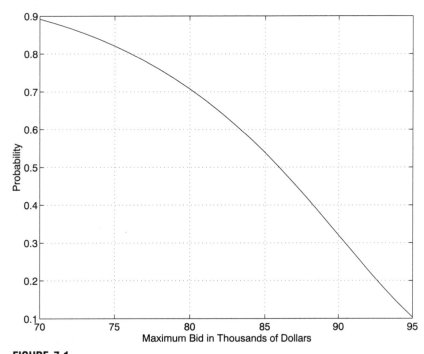

FIGURE 7.1

EXAMPLE 7.13

A Variation of the Bidding Problem

A family is seeking bids from general contractors for construction of a home. There are five potential bidders, each with probability 0.6 of bidding. Bids in thousands of dollars are iid, uniform [70, 120]. What is the probability of at least one bid of 85 or less?

Solution

$P(Y > 85) = (120 - 85)/50 = 0.7$. $g_N(s) = (0.4 + 0.6s)^5$.

———————————— MATLAB Script ————————————

```
>> P = 1 - (0.4 + 0.6*0.7)^5
P =   0.6293
```

Note that this problem could have been solved as a random number of Bernoulli trials, with probability of success $p = (85 - 70)/50 = 0.3$.

BERNOULLI TRIALS WITH RANDOM EXECUTION TIMES OR COSTS

Consider a sequence of Bernoulli trials executed sequentially in time with execution times (or costs) iid random quantities. We wish to determine the distribution of the time (or cost) to complete the first success. If N is the number of the trial on which the first success occurs, we have, formally

$$T = Y_1 + Y_2 + \cdots + Y_N$$

The random variable $N - 1 \sim$ geometric (p), where p is the probability of success on any trial. The total time T is just the composite demand. We use the basic result

$$M_T(s) = g_N[M_Y(s)] \quad \text{or} \quad g_T(s) = g_N[g_Y(s)] \quad \text{with } g_N(s) = \frac{ps}{1 - qs}$$

This takes convenient forms in two special cases:

1. If $Y_i \sim$ exponential (λ), then $T \sim$ exponential $(p\lambda)$.
2. If $Y_i - 1 \sim$ geometric (p_0), then $T - 1 \sim$ geometric $(p_0 p)$.

The proof of each case amounts to substitution and algebraic rearrangement of M_T or g_T, as the case may be, to show that it has the desired form. In the general case, solving for the distribution of T requires transform theory and may be handled best by a program such as MAPLE or Mathematica.

For the case of simple Y_i, we may use approximation procedures based on properties of the geometric series. Since $N - 1 \sim$ geometric (p),

$$g_N(s) = \frac{ps}{1 - qs} = ps \sum_{k=0}^{\infty} (qs)^k$$

$$= ps \left[\sum_{k=0}^{n} (qs)^k + \sum_{k=n+1}^{\infty} (qs)^k \right] = ps \left[\sum_{k=0}^{n} (qs)^k + (qs)^{n+1} \sum_{k=0}^{\infty} (qs)^k \right]$$

$$= ps \left[\sum_{k=0}^{n} (qs)^k \right] + (qs)^{n+1} g_N(s) = g_n(s) + (qs)^{n+1} g_N(s)$$

Note that $g_n(s)$ has the form of the generating function for a simple approximation N_n which matches values and probabilities with N up to $k = n$. Now

$$g_T(s) = g_n[g_Y(s)] + (qs)^{n+1} g_N[g_Y(s)]$$

The evaluation involves convolution of coefficients which effectively sets $s = 1$. Thus,

$$(qs)^{n+1} g_N[g_Y(s)] \quad \text{for} \quad s = 1 \text{ reduces to } q^{n+1} = P(N > n)$$

which is negligible if n is large enough. Suitable n may be determined in each case. If the Y_i are nonnegative, integer-valued, we may use the genD procedure on $g_n[g_Y(s)]$, where

$$g_n(s) = ps + pqs^2 + pq^2 s^3 + \cdots + pq^n s^{n+1}$$

For the general case of simple Y_i, in principle we could use mgD also. However, unless q is small, the number of terms needed to approximate g_n is likely to be too great.

EXAMPLE 7.14
Approximating the Generating Function

Let $p = 0.3$ and Y be uniformly distributed on $\{1, 2, \ldots, 10\}$. Determine the distribution for

$$T = \sum_{k=1}^{N} Y_k$$

Solution

———————————————— MATLAB Script ————————————————

```
>> p = 0.3;
>> q = 1 - p;
>> a = [30 35 40];        % Check for suitable n
>> b = q.^a
b =   1.0e-04 *            % Use n = 40
      0.2254    0.0379    0.0064
```

Continues

```
>> n = 40;
>> t = 0:n;
>> pY = 0.1*[0 ones(1,10)];
>> pN = p*[0 q.^t];            % Probabilities 0 <= k <= 41
>> genD
Do not forget zero coefficients for missing powers

Enter probabilities for N pN

Enter probabilities for Y pY
Values of D are in row matrix k; probabilities are in pD.
To view the distribution, call for gD.
>> sum(pD)                     % Check sum of probabilities
ans =  1.0000
FD = cumsum(pD);               % Distribution function for D
>> plot(0:100,FD(1:101))       % See Figure 7.2
----------                     % Commands for title, etc.
>> P50 = (k <= 50)*pD'
P50 =  0.9497
>> P30 = (k <= 30)*pD'
P30 =  0.8263
```

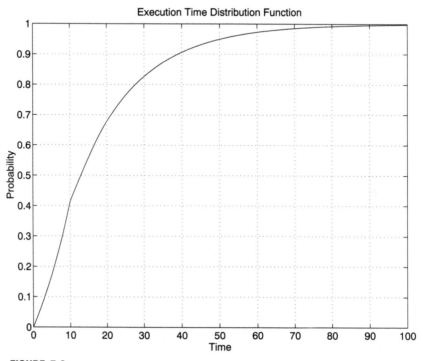

FIGURE 7.2

4. APPENDIX—SOME THEORETICAL DETAILS

■

1. **Proof of the formula for g_D.**

$$D = \sum_{k=0}^{N} Y_k = \sum_{n=0}^{\infty} I_{\{N=n\}} X_n$$

$$g_D(s) = E[s^D] = \sum_{n=0}^{\infty} E[I_{\{N=n\}} s^{X_n}] = \sum_{n=0}^{\infty} P(N = n) E[s^{X_n}]$$

$$= \sum_{n=0}^{\infty} P(N = n) g_Y(s)^n = g_N[g_Y(s)]$$

A parallel argument holds for M_D.

2. **Proof of the formulas for expectation and variance.**

$$E[D] = E\left[\sum_{n=0}^{\infty} I_{\{N=n\}} X_n \right] = \sum_{n=0}^{\infty} P(N = n) E[X_n]$$

$$= E[Y] \sum_{n=0}^{\infty} n P(N = n) = E[Y] E[N]$$

$$E[D^2] = \sum_{n=0}^{\infty} P(N = n) E[X_n^2] = \sum_{n=0}^{\infty} P(N = n) \{\mathrm{Var}[X_n] + E[X_n]^2\}$$

$$= \sum_{n=0}^{\infty} P(N = n) \{n\,\mathrm{Var}[Y] + n^2 E[Y]^2\} = E[N]\,\mathrm{Var}[Y] + E[N^2] E[Y]^2$$

Hence,

$$\mathrm{Var}[D] = E[N]\,\mathrm{Var}[Y] + E[N^2]E[Y]^2 - E[N]^2 E[Y]^2$$
$$= E[N]\,\mathrm{Var}[Y] + \mathrm{Var}[N] E[Y]^2$$

3. **Proof of the formulas for extreme values.**

a. $\{V_N > t\} = \bigcup_{n=0}^{\infty} \{N = n\}\{V_n > t\}$. By additivity and independence of $\{N, V_n\}$ for each n

$$P(V_N > t) = \sum_{n=0}^{\infty} P(N = n) P(V_n > t)$$

$$= \sum_{n=1}^{\infty} P(N = n) P(Y > t)^n, \quad \text{since } P(V_0 > t) = 0$$

If we add into the last sum the term $P(N = 0) P(Y > t)^0 = P(N = 0)$ and then subtract it, we have

$$P(V_N > t) = \sum_{n=0}^{\infty} P(N = n) P(Y > t)^n - P(N = 0)$$
$$= g_N[P(Y > t)] - P(N = 0)$$

b. A similar argument holds for proposition (b). In this case, we do not have the extra term for $\{N = 0\}$, since $P(W_0 \le t) = 1$.

REINFORCEMENT EXERCISES AND EXPLORATION PROBLEMS

—■—

REINFORCEMENT EXERCISES

P7.1 A composite demand D has counting random variable N which takes on values 1 through 5, with respective probabilities 0.156, 0.323, 0.334, 0.156, and 0.031. Each "customer" buys 1, 3, 4, or 6 items, with respective probabilities 0.15, 0.35, 0.30, and 0.20. Determine the distribution for D. What is the probability $7 \leq D \leq 18$?

P7.2 The number N of customers in a major appliance store is equally likely to be 1, 2, 3, 4, or 5. Each customer buys 0, 1, or 2 items with probabilities 0.3, 0.4, and 0.3, respectively. Determine the distribution on the number of items sold. What is the probability three or more are sold?

P7.3 Suppose each customer in the Problem P7.2 spends $0, $150, $325, $550, or $750 with respective probabilities 0.3, 0.1, 0.2, 0.2, and 0.2. Determine the probability distribution for the total demand D. What is the probability $D \geq 1500$? How many different values (including zero) can D have?

P7.4 A simple game is played with one six-sided die. The die is thrown once, yielding 1, 2, 3, 4, 5, or 6 on an equally likely basis. The player gets as many additional throws as the number on the first throw. Thus, if a three turns up, the player then gets three additional throws. His score, a random variable X, is the total number of points on the additional throws (not counting the initial throw).

a. Determine the distribution for X, the mean value $E[X]$, the variance $\text{Var}[X]$, and $P(X \geq 20)$.

b. Suppose the player is paid off as follows: $4.00 for 1 through 6 points, $7.00 for 7 through 12 points, $10.00 for 13 through 18 points, $15.00 for 19 through 24 points, $20.00 for 25 through 30 points, and $25.00 for more than 30 points. If G is the payoff random variable, determine its distribution. What should the player pay to make it a fair game?

P7.5 Experience indicates the number of ships passing a check point at a harbor entrance in a one-hour period may be represented by a random variable with the distribution

$k =$	0	1	2	3	4	5
$P(N = k) =$	0.01	0.03	0.07	0.14	0.18	0.18
$k =$	6	7	8	9	10	
$P(N = k) =$	0.16	0.11	0.06	0.04	0.02	

The ships pay an inspection fee according to various classifications. The amounts (in hundreds of dollars) may be represented by $\{Y_i : 1 \leq i\}$ iid, with distribution

$k =$	1	3	5	7
$P(Y = k) =$	0.3	0.4	0.2	0.1

Under the usual assumptions, determine the distribution for the random variable D which represents the total fees for ships arriving in a one-hour period. What is the probability that the total fees for ships arriving in that period will be at least $2000?

P7.6 The number of customers in a day who consider a certain item in a shop may be represented by a random variable N. The customers buy independently, with the same distribution. Let Y_i be the amount purchased by the ith customer. Assume

N takes on values 0, 1, 2, 3, 4, or 5, with respective probabilities 0.05, 0.40, 0.30, 0.15, 0.07, and 0.03

Y_i takes on values 0, 1, 2, or 3, with respective probabilities 0.05, 0.50, 0.30, and 0.15

Determine the distribution of the number D of items sold in a day. Determine $E[D]$ and $Var[D]$ both from the distribution and by the formulas detemined in the text.

P7.7 Experience has shown that the number of parties which arrive at a certain restaurant on Tuesday evenings may be represented by a random variable N which is Poisson (30). The number of persons in the ith party is Y_i. Suppose $\{Y_i: 1 <= i\}$ is iid, with $P(Y_i = k) = p_k$ as follows:

$$p_k = 0.05,\ 0.3,\ 0.1,\ 0.25,\ 0.05,\ 0.1,\ 0.05,\ 0.1$$

for k from 1 to 8, respectively. Under the usual assumptions:

a. What is the expected number of customers?
b. What is the probability there will be no more than five parties of eight?
c. What is the expected number of four-person parties?

P7.8 A mail-order house purchases boxes for a thirty-day period. Previous records show that the number of customer orders in a thirty-day period may be represented as a random quantity N which is Poisson (500). Customer orders are shipped in one of five kinds of boxes, depending upon the physical size of the order. The unit costs of the five types of boxes (in dollars) are 0.10, 0.25, 0.35, 0.50, and 0.80, respectively. Customer "demand" for the boxes is iid, with probabilities 0.3, 0.3, 0.2, 0.1, and 0.1 for the five types, respectively.

a. What is the expected cost of boxes for the thirty-day period?
b. What is the probability that the total cost for boxes of the fourth type will be more than $25?

P7.9   A discount retail store has two outlets in Houston, with a common warehouse. Customer requests are phoned to the warehouse for pickup. Two items, a and b, are featured in a special sale. The number of orders in a day from store A is $N_A \sim$ Poisson (30); from store B, the number of orders is $N_B \sim$ Poisson (40). For Store A, the probability of an order for Item a is 0.3, and for Item b is 0.7. For Store B, the probability of an order for Item a is 0.4, and for Item b is 0.6. What is the probability the total order for Item b in a day is 50 or more?

P7.10   A caterer is planning for a banquet. The number of guests is not known at the time of preliminary planning but is represented by a random quantity $N \sim$ Poisson (50). Guests will be offered a choice of entree. They order independently and it is assumed that the probabilities for steak, chicken, and fish are 0.7, 0.2, and 0.1, respectively. What is the probability 10 or more will order fish? What is the expected number of steak orders? What is the probability of more orders for fish than for chicken?

P7.11   The number of lightning strikes during a severe thunderstorm over a national forest area is a random quantity $N \sim$ Poisson (100). Experience shows the strikes may be considered to form a Bernoulli sequence independent of N, with probability $p = 0.005$ that any strike will start a fire. If F is the number of fires started during a storm, determine $P(F \geq 2)$, $P(F \geq 5)$.

P7.12   The number N of orders a day forwarded to the shipping department of a book dealer is Poisson (100). The individual orders constitute an iid class, with each Y_i having values 1, 2, 5, 10, 20, 50, and 100, with respective probabilities 0.1, 0.15, 0.15, 0.25, 0.20, 0.10, and 0.05.

a. What is the expected number of books shipped in a day?
b. What is the probability there will be no more than six orders of 100 books?
c. What is the expected number of 50 book orders?

P7.13   The number N of offers for a home for sale is a random variable with values one through six, with respective probabilities 0.1, 0.2, 0.3, 0.2, 0.1, and 0.1. The amounts offered (in thousands of dollars) may be considered iid, N(100, 400). What is the probability the maximum offer will be at least 120?

Note that although the gaussian distribution can take on negative values, the probability of negative values in this case is less than 10^{-6}, which is quite negligible.

P7.14   Bids are opened on a machine tool. There are five potential bidders, with probability 0.6 that each will bid. The amounts they bid (in thousands of dollars) are iid uniform [70, 120]. What is the probability that there will be at least one bid for 100 or more?

Remark: At least two approaches suggest themselves. One is to deal with extreme values. Another is to treat this as a random number of Bernoulli trials, with a bid of 100 or more a success.

P7.15 Bids are opened on a construction job. There are five potential bidders, with probability 0.5 that each will bid. The amounts they bid (in thousands of dollars) are iid uniform [90, 130]. What is the probability that there will be at least one bid for 100 or less?

Note that receipt of zero bids does not result in a bid of 100 or less.

P7.16 Suppose a teacher of applied probability is equally likely to have 0, 1, 2, or 3 students come in during office hours on a given day. If the visit times (in minutes) of individual students are iid exponential (0.1), what is the probability that no visit will last more than 20 minutes?

P7.17 The number N of noise bursts on a data transmission line in an hour of operation is Poisson (μ). The number of digit errors caused by the ith burst is a random variable Y_i. An error correcting system is capable of correcting five or fewer errors in a burst. Under the usual assumptions, with $Y_i - 1 \sim$ geometric ($p = 0.5$) and $\mu = 10$, what is the probability of no uncorrected error in an hour of operation?

Hint: There are no uncorrected errors iff the maximum number of errors in the bursts does not exceed five.

P7.18 Suppose the number N of jobs brought to a service center in a week is geometric ($p = 0.01$). Service times are iid, independent of N. If the time Y_i, in hours, for the ith service is exponential $\lambda = 2$, what is the probability that at least one job time will exceed two hours?

P7.19 The number N of bids on a painting is binomial (10, 0.3). The bid amounts (in thousands of dollars) Y_i form an iid class, with common density function $f_Y(t) = 0.005(37 - 2t)$, $2 \le t \le 10$. What is the probability that the maximum amount bid is greater than $5,000?

P7.20 The number of noise pulses on a line in a one-hour period is a random variable $N \sim$ Poisson (100). The distribution of the peak voltages on successive pulses may be represented by an iid sequence $\{Y_i : 1 \le i\}$, exponential (0.01).

a. What is the probability that five or more pulses will exceed 300 volts?
b. What is the probability the maximum voltage in the one-hour period will be 500 volts or more?

P7.21 Five solid state modules are installed in a computer system. If the modules are not defective, they have practically unlimited life. However, with probability $p = 0.05$, any unit could have a defect that results in a lifetime, in hours, which is exponential (0.0025). What is the probability that no module fails in the first 500 hours?

Note: For an alternate approach, see the solution to part (a) of Reinforcement Problem P3.14.

P7.22 As a sales inducement, an electronics store offers each customer who makes a purchase of 100 dollars or more a free chance at a prize. This is in the form of a "drawing," so that the prize is available immediately. Suppose the time between sales (hence drawings) is exponential ($\lambda = 4$). The probability of winning on any draw is 0.01. If the times between sales are independent, what is the probability of a winner in an eight-hour day? What is the expected time between winning drawings?

P7.23 A company recruiter interviews students in a university placement center. The time in hours for each interview is a random quantity exponential (3). Under the usual assumptions, what is the probability that the interviewer will see at least fifteen students in six hours of interviewing? What is the probability that no interview will last for more than one hour?

APPENDIX A: Getting Started with MATLAB

PREVIEW

Use of the material in this book does not require programming in MATLAB beyond entering data in the appropriate forms. Examples included in the text should make clear how this is to be done in each case. The user defined procedures and functions are described in the text and the files for these are included on the disk that accompanies this book. All that is necessary is to copy these files into the appropriate directory.

The programs operate equally well on any platform and operating system—MS DOS, UNIX, X-Windows, Windows for PC, Macintosh, etc.—and the operation is the same in each case. This is one of many nice characteristics of MATLAB. We give a brief set of instructions for the operations required to use the files.

Users desiring a fuller understanding of MATLAB programming and the resources available should consult the Tutorial section in the *MATLAB User's Guide*. While there is a user's guide specific for each operating system, the differences are in the initial "getting started" sections. The Tutorial is the same in all cases. Not all topics in the Tutorial need be studied for use with this text. A list of some of the more useful topics is given.

INSTALLATION

████

MATLAB, or the student version of MATLAB, should be installed on your hard drive as described in the MATLAB documentation. The m-files containing the functions and procedures described in the text are included in the disk provided. This is formatted for a MS DOS machine (IBM compatible PC). The m-files are simple text files, which users of other operating systems should be able to access and copy.

The m-files should be copied to a directory on the MATLABPATH. Since the procedure varies with the operating system, you should consult the MATLAB documentation for your machine.

Once the m-files are copied and available to MATLAB, operation is simple and is the same on all machines. The following instructions should enable the beginner to get started.

USING MATLAB

████

1. Activate MATLAB. When the MATLAB prompt $>>$ appears, MATLAB is ready to accept input.
2. Input to MATLAB.
   a. Commands or data may be entered directly from the **keyboard**.
   b. Input may be obtained by calling **m-files**. These are text files which contain data and/or a series of MATLAB commands. They are identified to MATLAB by the suffix .m.

      These m-files may be created with a text editor. Except for data, the principal inputs will be the programs in the m-files provided on the disk accompanying the text.

      To utilize the data and/or MATLAB commands in filename.m, simply give the MATLAB command

      > > **filename**   (Omit the suffix .m.)

      Although the suffix .m is needed as part of the name of the file, *it should be omitted* in the MATLAB call for the contents of the file.
   c. User defined functions are in m-files of the same name. For example, the function cbinomial for computing cumulative terms in the binomial distribution is in the file **cbinomial.m**. This file begins with the line

      function y = cbinomial(n, p, k)

      followed on subsequent lines by a series of MATLAB commands to be carried out. On some lines there are comments after the symbol %. These are ignored by MATLAB but give information in cryptic form to the user. The quantities n and p are the parameters for the binomial distribution. The parameter k may be a row vector of integers, between 0 and n. Suppose $n = 10$, $p = 0.37$, and $k = [4\ 5\ 7\ 9]$. Give the command

$$>> \mathbf{P = cbinomial(10, 0.3, [4\ 5\ 7\ 9])}$$

After a brief interval, which depends upon the speed of the machine, the program responds with

$$P = 0.5400 \quad 0.2939 \quad 0.0356 \quad 0.0009$$

These are the respective probabilities: $P(X \geq 4)$, $P(X \geq 5)$, $P(X \geq 7)$, $P(X \geq 9)$.

3. If you wish to see the *contents* of one of the m-files while in MAT-LAB, give the MATLAB command

$$>> \textbf{type filename.m} \qquad \text{(The suffix.m } may \text{ be omitted.)}$$

4. In order to *print* or *edit* a MATLAB session, *record* it in a file in your home directory with the **diary** command. When you are ready to begin recording, first clear the MATLAB workspace with the command

$$>> \textbf{clear}$$

Although it is not necessary, it may be desirable to clear the window with the command

$$>> \textbf{clc}$$

Then use the MATLAB command

$$>> \textbf{diary filename}$$

The ensuing material in the MATLAB window will be recorded in a file called filename. To end the recording and make the file available, use the MATLAB command

$$>> \textbf{diary off}$$

Since the newly created file is a text file, it may be edited and its contents may be printed according to the usual procedures for printing a text file.

5. Creating and printing MATLAB graphics.

The professional version 4.1a of MATLAB has elaborate and sophisticated graphic capabilities. Version 3.5 has somewhat more restricted capabilities. However, we use only simple plots of one or more graphs on a single graph sheet. The following information should be sufficient for most purposes. More complete information can be obtained from the Graphics section of the Tutorial in the *MATLAB User's Guide.*

The **plot** command can be used to produce simple graphs. If you specify two vectors (row matrices) x, y as arguments, the command **plot**(x, y) produces a plot of y versus x. Use of the **hold** command allows multiple plots of data with a specified line style for each set of data. For example, suppose $t = 0 : 0.01 : 1$; $y1 = \text{sqrt}(t)$, and $y2 = t\char`^2$. The commands

$$>> \textbf{plot}(t, y1)$$
$$>> \textbf{hold on}$$
$$>> \textbf{plot}(t, y2, \text{`--'})$$
$$>> \textbf{hold off}$$

produce plots of $y1$ vs t and $y2$ vs t, with the first line solid and the second dashed.

You may put *title and axis labels* on the graphics window with the following MATLAB commands:

$$>> \textbf{title}(\text{`Your Title'})$$
$$>> \textbf{xlabel}(\text{`Horizontal'})$$
$$>> \textbf{ylabel}(\text{`Verticle'})$$

The single quotes are necessary; the actual text between the single quotes will appear on the graph in the appropriate places.

You may put *gridlines* on the graph by using the MATLAB command

$$>> \textbf{grid}$$

You may *print* the graphics window on a *laser printer*. The MATLAB command is simply

$$>> \textbf{print} \qquad \text{(No filename is needed.)}$$

SOME FEATURES OF MATLAB

MATLAB works with rectangular *matrices*.

A one by one matrix is referred to as a *scalar*. A row matrix or a column matrix is referred to as a *vector,* with the designation row or column where needed for clarity.

The basic structure of a command is

$$\text{Variable} = \text{expression}$$

The variable is given a "name" (usually a few letters). The expression may be a matrix with data or may involve other variables and functions. If the input after the MATLAB prompt $>>$ is an expression, MATLAB assigns it the name ans. The matrix corresponding to the variable is stored in the MATLAB workspace, where it can be called in other expressions.

A variable name can be reassigned by equating it to a new expression. This expression can include the current variable by that name.

EXAMPLE

Suppose it is desired to create a three by five probability matrix whose terms sum to one. We could first use the MATLAB function rand to generate a matrix with random terms. Then we could divide each term by the total of all terms in the first matrix. The MATLAB function sum gives the total of the elements in a vector; for a rectangular matrix it produces a row vector of the column sums. We thus need to apply it twice to get the total of the elements of a rectangular matrix.

─────────────── MATLAB Script ───────────────

```
>> P = rand(3,5)          % Call for generating a random matrix
P =
    0.2190    0.6793    0.5194    0.0535    0.0077
    0.0470    0.9347    0.8310    0.5297    0.3834
    0.6789    0.3835    0.0346    0.6711    0.0668
>> P = P/sum(sum(P))      % Reassignment of the variable P
P =
    0.0363    0.1125    0.0860    0.0089    0.0013
    0.0078    0.1548    0.1376    0.0877    0.0635
    0.1124    0.0635    0.0057    0.1111    0.0111
>> sum(sum(P))            % Check on the total of the new P
ans = 1.0000
```

MATLAB OPERATIONS

It is not necessary to work through all of the material in the Tutorial. The following operations are used and illustrated in the text—in both m-files and the worked examples. For most purposes, examination of these should suffice. If more information is desired, consult the tutorial under the relevant topics.

1. **Matrix Operations.** The standard matrix operations of transposing, adding, subtracting, multiplying, dividing, and using powers.
2. **Array Operations.** These are element by element operations, usually indicated by a period (.) before the operator. For example, C = A.*B is a matrix whose elements are the products of corresponding elements of A and B.
3. **Relational Operations.** Compares two matrices of equal dimensions. For example, M = A == B is a matrix with ones where A and B agree and zeros elsewhere. Such a matrix can be used in a variety of ways as illustrated repeatedly in the examples.

4. **Logical Operations.** These operations are applied to zero-one matrices with the same dimensions. &, |, and ∼ correspond to the "and," "or," and "not" logical operations. We utilize these in handling minterm vectors (see Chapter 1).

5. **Subscripting and Generating Matrices and Vectors.** Although these are illustrated repeatedly in the text, it may be desirable to review these topics in the Tutorial in the section on Vector and Matrix Manipulation.

6. **Functions.** MATLAB provides a wide array of functions, some of which are employed as subroutines in the user defined functions and procedures in this text. If you plan to develop your own procedures and functions, you may find it helpful to have the MATLAB Reference Guide, which gives descriptions of the standard functions included with MATLAB. There are others in the optional specialized "Toolboxes."

FINAL COMMENT

Experience has shown that even novices on the computer can learn to use the programs described in the text and provided on the disk with very little difficulty. After reading the preceding introductory instructions on MATLAB and working through the examples, the beginner should soon come "up to speed." Working the problems at the end of the chapters should lead to increasing facility with the programs as well as to new insights into the probability model. Those who want to expand their use of MATLAB and modify existing programs or write new ones should make use of the Tutorial section of the MATLAB User's Guide. The topics noted above are particularly relevant.

Index

gaussian distribution. *See* normal distribution

generating function for compound demand, 154
  procedure: genD, 156

independence of events, 41–43
  equivalent conditions, 41
  k of *n* independent events, 49–50
    function: ckn, 49
    function: ikn, 49
  minterm probabilities, 42
    function: imintest, 48
    function: minprob, 45
  product rule, 42
  replacement rule, 42
independent random variables, 125–127, 131–133
  general procedures, 131–133
    procedure: isimple, 131–132
  tests for independence, 125–127
    function: idbn, 125
    procedure: ijdbn, 125
    procedure: itest, 126
indicator function, 6, 29–30
  for Boolean combinations, 30
  minterm vectors, 30
  properties, 29
  simple random variables, 101–102

joint simple random variables, 115 ff
  calculations of standard parameters, 119–122
    conditional expectation, 122
    covariance, 121
    expectation, 120
    marginal distributions, 120
    regression line, 122
    variance, 121
  distribution matrices X, Y, P, 116
  functions of X and Y, 122–124
    conditional expectation, 124
    procedure ezx, 124
    distribution for g(X,Y), 123
    procedure jgdbn, 123
  general procedure, 128–131
    procedure: jsimple, 128–129
  t, u matrices, 116–117
    procedure: jcalc (and jcalcd), 117

validity of P matrix, 119
  function: jdtest, 119

minterm, 5–6
  fundamental partition, 5
  expansion, 6
  maps, 2, 6, 8, 13–14
minterm expansion, 6
  simple random variables, 101
minterm probabilities, 12 ff
  boolean combinations, 12–25
    procedure: mincalc, 25–27
    procedure: mincalct, 27–28
  independent events, 42
    function: ckn, 49
    function: ikn, 49–50
    function: imintest, 48
    function: minprob, 45
minterm vector, 8–9, 29–30
  function: mintable, 10
  function: minterm, 9
  function: minvec, 11
moment generating function for compound demand, 154
  procedure: mgD, 160
multinomial distribution, 87–91
  procedure: multinomial, 89
  relation to the binomial distribution, 88

normal distribution, 82–83
  approximation to the binomial distribution, 83
  approximation to the gamma distribution, 83
  approximation to the Poisson distribution, 83
  central limit theorem, 83

Poisson counting process, 153–154
Poisson decomposition, 163–165
Poisson distribution, 79–81
  approximation to the binomial distribution, 79, 80–81, 93
  relation to the gamma distribution, 79, 82, 93
probability system, 2–3

random sums, 152, 154–155
  compound demand, 152, 154
  generating function, 154
    procedure: genD, 156

INDEX

Thank you for your interest in the **BookWare Companion Series** and *Basic Probability Problems Using MATLAB®* by Paul E. Pfeiffer. We would appreciate if it you would answer some questions for us.

I ordered this book for: Personal use ____; Course adoption consideration ____; Both ____

On which platforms does your department/school use MATLAB®? Check all applicable: PC ___; Mac ___

Do you plan to adopt this book for a course? Yes ___; No ___; Course No._____; Enrollment_____;
Course Title_____

Text(s) most recently used _____

How is MATLAB® provided? Check all applicable: Site license _____ Student Edition _____

What other applications would you like to see in future volumes in the **BookWare** series? MathCAD ____;
Maple____; Mathematica____; Matrix X ____; X-Math ____; Other (indicate)_____

Name _____
Perm. Address   School Address
_____   _____
_____   _____

Telephone: _____   E-mail _____

If you have an idea for improving the BC concept, an example problem, a demonstration using software or multimedia, or a new proposal, contact us today.
Yes, I wish to become involved as a reviewer ___ with suggestions ___ with an idea to explore ____

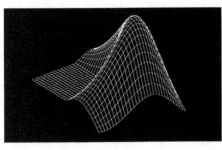

MATLAB® Technical Computing Environment

R-BK-PFE

MATLAB, the software presented in **Basic Probability Topics Using MATLAB** by Paul E. Pfeiffer (PWS Publishing, 1995), is a powerful yet easy-to-use system for interactive numeric computation, data analysis, and graphics. Widely used in academia, industry, and government, MATLAB has become the premier technical computing environment for electrical engineering, applied math, physics, and other disciplines.

- **MATLAB Application Toolboxes** add functions for symbolic math, signal processing, control design, neural networks, and other areas.
- **The Student Edition** is a limited-matrix-size version of MATLAB for use on students' own personal computers.
- **Educational discount plans** support classroom instruction and research.
- **Classroom Kits** provide cost-effective support for PC or Mac teaching labs.
- **MATLAB-based books** use MATLAB to illustrate basic and advanced material in a wide range of topics.

NAME _____

TITLE _____

COMPANY _____

DEPT. OR M/S _____

STREET _____

CITY/STATE/ZIP _____

PHONE _____

FAX _____ EMAIL _____

WHERE DID YOU PURCHASE THIS BOOK? _____

Computer platform – check all that apply:
❑ PC/Macintosh   ❑ UNIX Workstation   ❑ VAX/Supercomputer

▶ **For the fastest response, fax this card to The MathWorks:**
(508) 653-6284, or call (508) 653-1415.

I am interested in The MathWorks product information for:

❑ Simulation	❑ Control System Design	❑ Math & Visualization
❑ Signal Processing	❑ Symbolic Math	❑ Educational Discounts
❑ System Identification	❑ Chemometrics	❑ Classroom Kits
❑ Neural Networks	❑ Optimization	❑ Student Edition
❑ Statistics	❑ Image Processing	❑ MATLAB Books

BUSINESS REPLY MAIL
FIRST CLASS MAIL PERMIT NO. 5438 BOSTON, MA

POSTAGE HAS BEEN PREPAID

PWS Publishing Company
20 Park Plaza
Boston, MA 02116
Attn: Ken Morton

NO POSTAGE
NECESSARY
IF MAILED
IN THE
UNITED STATES

BUSINESS REPLY MAIL
FIRST CLASS MAIL PERMIT NO. 5438 BOSTON, MA

POSTAGE HAS BEEN PREPAID

PWS Publishing Company
20 Park Plaza
Boston, MA 02116
Attn: Ken Morton

PWS PUBLISHING COMPANY
LICENSE AGREEMENT

This is a legal agreement between you, the program user, and PWS Publishing Company (the Publisher). By opening the attached sealed disk package, you are agreeing to the terms of this agreement. If you do not agree to these terms, promptly return the sealed disk package and all accompanying materials.

Grant of License

PWS Publishing Company grants you the right to use one copy of the enclosed software program and data files ("Software") on one microcomputer at a time. You may not network the Software or otherwise use it on more than one computer at a time without obtaining a site license from the Publisher.

Copyright

The Software is owned by the Publisher and is protected by United States copyright. You may not copy the Software in whole or in part except that you may: (a) make one copy of the Software solely for back-up purposes, or (b) transfer the Software to a single hard disk or other mass-storage device provided that you keep the original solely for backup purposes. You may not copy any written materials that accompany the Software.

Other Restrictions

You may not rent, lease, lend, or otherwise distribute copies of the Software to others. The Software license may not be transferred to others except by written permission of the Publisher. You may not reverse engineer, decompile, or disassemble the Software.

Limited Warranty

The warranty for the enclosed disk(s) is for ninety (90) days. If, during that time period, you find defects in workmanship or material, the Publisher will replace the defective item. THE PUBLISHER AND THE AUTHOR PROVIDE NO OTHER WARRANTIES, EXPRESSED OR IMPLIED, AND SHALL NOT BE LIABLE FOR ANY DAMAGES, SPECIAL, INDIRECT, INCIDENTAL, CONSEQUENTIAL, OR OTHERWISE ARISING OUT OF THE USE OR INABILITY TO USE THIS SOFTWARE.

For warranty service or additional information about PWS Publishing Company's licensing policies, contact:

Technology Services
511 Forest Lodge Road
Pacific Grove, CA 93950-5098
(408) 649-1570
Fax: (408) 375-6414

For damaged disk replacement *only*, contact:

ITP Educational Division Customer Service
(800) 354-9706